Thornes Classic Short

SHORT STORIES

by

ARTHUR CONAN DOYLE

EDITED BY SARAH MATTHEWS

SERIES EDITOR: MIKE ROYSTON

Stanley Thornes (Publishers) Ltd

A Scandal in Bohemia first published 1891.
The Speckled Band first published 1892.
The Dancing Men first published 1903.

This edition first published in 1996 by:
Stanley Thornes (Publishers) Ltd
Ellenborough House
Wellington Street
CHELTENHAM GL50 1YW
England

96 97 98 99 00 / 10 9 8 7 6 5 4 3 2

A catalogue record for this book is available from the British Library.

ISBN 0–7487–2483–4

Acknowledgements

The author and publishers are grateful to the following for permission to reproduce illustrations and photographs:
Mansell Collection, pages 2 (top), 6, 7
Mary Evans Picture Library, pages 3, 4, 5

Typeset by DP Press, Kent
Illustrated by Trevor Parkin and Steve Ballinger (page 7)
Printed and bound in Great Britain at T J Press (Padstow) Ltd, Cornwall

Contents

How to use this book

This book contains three short stories by Arthur Conan Doyle. It is designed so that you can read the stories on your own, or share your reading with others. Whichever way you read, the stories have been chosen above all to be *enjoyed*.

The Introduction contains:

- a brief account of the writer's life. This gives you an impression of the kind of person he was and outlines the most important things that happened to him during his lifetime.

- a background to the stories, in words and pictures. This tells you about the kind of stories they are, the main characters in them, and where they took place.

To help you get the most from them, the stories have been presented in a particular way. They contain the following features:

- boxes at the beginning of each story, and at other key points, which suggest what you should look out for as you read.

- a glossary at the foot of every page giving the meanings of words you may find unfamiliar.

- a commentary summarising what is happening on each page of the story, to help you follow it as you read.

During each story, you will now and again come across a 'Pause for Playback' section. This contains brief questions to highlight important points in the part of the story you have just read. You can make up your own mind about the 'answers'. They do not have to be written down.

After each story, there is a Study guide. This contains activities designed to help you form an understanding of the story as a whole. Some activities are for small groups, some are for pairs, and some for doing by yourself.

At the end of the book, you will find an Overview section. This asks you to think further about how the stories are written and to make some comparisons between them.

Enjoy your reading!

Introduction

ABOUT THE WRITER

S ir Arthur Conan Doyle is best
known as the creator of the
master-detective Sherlock Holmes,
but he did not really want his
detective stories to be his main
claim to fame. In fact, he did not
start his working life as a writer at
all, but as a doctor.

Arthur Doyle was born in
1859, the son of parents who had
more hopes of social success than
money to achieve them. Doyle's
father was the youngest, and least
successful, son of a professional
family, while his mother was
concerned with establishing the Doyle
connection with various aristocratic
families in Ireland. Doyle himself was
strong, keen at sports, and with a
patchy but sufficient education.

Sir Arthur Conan Doyle

Doyle's coat of arms, on a bookplate

After leaving school, he qualified as a
doctor in 1881, and soon got a job as
doctor on a whaling ship. The people that
he met there, tough seafaring men,
provided him with models for many of the
characters in his stories. However, it was
clear that he would never make a very
good living as a doctor on board ship. He
returned to England and eventually
joined a practice in Southsea, on the
outskirts of Portsmouth, in the south of
England.

At the time when Doyle began working
as a doctor, medicine was by no means as
well-regulated or as scientific as it has since
become, and Doyle was not happy with

the mixture of showmanship and deception necessary to make a decent living. He was never a very successful doctor. In 1885 he married, and the limited income he could make was barely enough to support his enlarged household, particularly when his daughter was born in 1889. He had always written stories and novels, though little that he had written had been accepted for publication. But then he managed to sell a story, *The Study in Scarlet*, the first of the Sherlock Holmes series. Although it did not make his fortune overnight, this and his next story, *The Sign of Four*, were sufficiently successful to give him the courage to abandon medicine and to dedicate himself full-time to writing.

After that he never really looked back and, although he occasionally resented being labelled as the creator of the Great Detective, as though he was incapable of writing anything else, the fact was that Holmes had an appeal that resisted every attempt by Doyle to put an end to him. Even after he had apparently killed Holmes off in a story called *The Final Problem*, he soon had to bring him back to life again, and write several more volumes of Holmes stories.

In between writing the Holmes stories, Doyle wrote stories about other characters and other times. These included the dashing Brigadier Gerard, and the scientist, Professor Challenger, who appeared in Doyle's novel *The Lost World*, in which Challenger and his companions explore a secret area of South America where dinosaurs still survive.

In 1900, Doyle volunteered his services to the government during the Boer War in South Africa. His actions during the war, and his support of the government's policy, earned him a knighthood.

There was one other major interest in Doyle's life. He believed strongly in the spirit world, and in the ability of the dead to communicate with the living. He died in 1930. He had promised that, after his death, he would send a message to his loved ones. As yet, there is no record of it having reached them.

An early illustration of Holmes and Watson from the Strand *magazine*

DETECTIVES AND DETECTIVE STORIES

Sherlock Holmes is a private detective, called upon when the regular police are at a loss, or are not thought sufficiently discreet to handle delicate and sensitive matters to do with governments or grand families.

The police as we understand them today were still fairly new at the time Doyle was writing, and detectives were an even more recent idea. It was only in 1843 that 'intelligent men…were selected…to form a body of individuals called the "detective force"' whose members sometimes dressed in the clothes 'of ordinary individuals' rather than in uniform. Within thirty years or so, as well as the regular detective force, there were a number of private detective agencies, whose members could be employed to find missing persons, investigate references, follow husbands and wives suspected of being unfaithful, and generally check up on events. Some of these agencies were very good; some were not.

Detectives, with their tendency to disguise themselves, to follow people and to watch them secretly, were regarded with a mixture of respect and suspicion. Particularly suspect was a French policeman called Eugène Vidocq, who published his memoirs in 1828. Vidocq had been a robber, an acrobat, a forger and a highwayman. After some unpleasantly close encounters with the law, including an eight-year sentence as a galley slave on a ship (from which he escaped), Vidocq became a police spy. He set up a methodical card-index system, and was one of the first policemen to take impressions of footprints. He was also a master of disguise. During his time with the police force he solved a number of burglaries, showing great skill and ingenuity, though the impressiveness of his achievements was rather diminished when it became known that he had probably organised the burglaries in the first place!

Vidocq was a great source of inspiration to authors of the newly developing form of crime fiction, and in particular he had a great influence on the American writer Edgar Allan Poe (1809–49). Doyle himself, as we shall see, was in turn greatly influenced by Poe.

Poe was fascinated by the offbeat, the gruesome and the grotesque. Vidocq's career, with its combination of cleverness and seedy underworld activities, appealed to him greatly. He used many of Vidocq's methods when creating his own detective, Dupin.

Nineteenth-century detectives arrest a criminal

Poe is regarded as being the originator of the modern crime story, and tales such as *The Murders in the rue Morgue*, *The Purloined Letter* and *The Gold Bug* are still a delight to read.

Doyle enjoyed Poe's writing a great deal, saying that his detective stories were 'wonderful in their masterful force and their quick dramatic point'. He used Poe as a model when he set out to write detective stories himself, basing a lot of Holmes's scientific method on Dupin, while traces of Vidocq's double-sided character, his methodical approach and his mastery of disguise, can be found in both Sherlock Holmes and in his arch-enemy, the fiendishly evil Professor Moriarty.

Just what is a detective story, though? There are all sorts of different kinds of stories – war stories, school stories, sports stories, fairy stories, detective stories – each of them written according to a different set of 'rules' requiring different kinds of characters, settings and events. The first thing that a detective story needs is, of course, a detective; a person clever enough to solve a problem or a crime that other

Moriarty – Holmes's arch-enemy – in The Final Problem

people find impossible to unravel. The other thing that they need is a problem; a crime that needs to be solved. The interest of the story for the reader is to try to solve the crime, picking up the clues which the author leaves scattered through the story, testing their own cleverness against the detective's. Last of all, every detective story has to have a solution and an explanation of how the problem was solved.

All in all, then, detective stories give their readers excitement, the pleasures of a puzzle, and the satisfaction of a solution. It is an art form which Conan Doyle developed exceptionally well.

Mysterious crime + Clever detective = Ingenious solution = Happy ending

PEOPLE AND PLACES IN THE SHERLOCK HOLMES STORIES

The main characters in Conan Doyle's Sherlock Holmes stories are Sherlock Holmes, the detective, and his close friend, Dr John Watson, who is usually the narrator of the stories.

Holmes and Watson first came together in the full-length detective novel, *A Study in Scarlet*. By that time, Holmes was already working as a detective in London, while Watson had returned to London after being invalided out of the Army Medical Corps, having been wounded in one of the Afghan Wars in northern India. Holmes and Watson got on well together, and soon started to share a flat at 221B Baker Street in London. It was Watson who told Holmes at the end of the events narrated in *A Study in Scarlet*, 'Your merits should be publicly recognised. You should publish an account of the case. If you won't, I will for you.' This was the beginning of a close association, lasting over many years, during which Holmes's standing as the Great Detective was established, not least due to the accounts of his cases put forward by the ever-admiring Dr Watson.

Dr John Watson, m.d.   *Sherlock Holmes*

The London in which Conan Doyle's Sherlock Holmes stories are set was a crowded, noisy, busy place. There were huge contrasts between areas of great wealth, with big houses and lovely gardens, and slum areas where people lived crowded together in desperate poverty. Some areas were lit by gas-light, transport was horse-drawn, and the coal-fires which warmed the houses often caused a heavy yellow fog to hang over the city.

London in the fog in about 1900

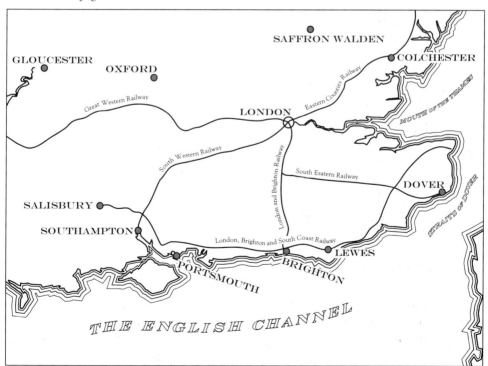

London and the south-east of England, showing the main railways in the late nineteeth century

A SCANDAL IN BOHEMIA

Look out for...
- the King of Bohemia. What is he like, and what does Sherlock Holmes think of him?
- Irene Adler. Why does she have such a strong and lasting effect on Holmes?

To Sherlock Holmes she is always *the* woman. I have seldom heard him mention her under any other name. In his eyes she eclipses and predominates the whole of her sex. It was not that he felt any emotion akin to love for Irene Adler. All emotions, and that one particularly, were abhorrent to his cold, precise, but admirably balanced mind. He was, I take it, the most perfect reasoning and observing machine that the world has seen; but, as a lover, he would have placed himself in a false position. He never spoke of the softer passions, save with a gibe and a sneer. They were admirable things for the observer – excellent for drawing the veil from men's motives and actions. But for the trained reasoner to admit such intrusions into his own delicate and finely adjusted temperament was to introduce a distracting factor which might throw a doubt upon all his mental results. Grit in a sensitive instrument, or a crack in one of his own high-power lenses, would not be more disturbing than a strong emotion in a nature such as his. And yet there was but one woman to him, and that woman was the late Irene Adler, of dubious and questionable memory.

COMMENTARY

Doctor Watson, who is telling the story, says there is one particular woman who is important to Holmes. This does not mean Holmes is in love with her. Love is an emotion which would disturb his thinking processes, and so he will not allow it into his life.

predominates: is superior to
akin to: like
abhorrent: hateful
gibe: mocking comment
of dubious and questionable memory: remembered as being someone who did not behave particularly well

I had seen little of Holmes since the singular chain of events which I have already narrated in a bold fashion under the heading of *The Sign of Four*. My marriage had, as he foretold, drifted us away from each other. My own complete happiness, and the home-centred interests which rise up around the man who first finds himself master of his own establishment, were sufficient to absorb all my attention; while Holmes, who loathed every form of society with his whole Bohemian soul, remained in our lodgings in Baker Street, buried among his old books, and alternating from week to week between cocaine and ambition, the drowsiness of the drug, and the fierce energy of his own keen nature. He was still, as ever, deeply attracted by the study of crime, and occupied his immense faculties and extraordinary powers of observation in following out those clues, and clearing up those mysteries, which had been abandoned as hopeless by the official police. From time to time I heard some vague account of his doings: of his summons to Odessa in the case of the Trepoff murder, of his clearing up of the singular tragedy of the Atkinson brothers at Trincomalee, and finally of the mission which he had accomplished so delicately and successfully for the reigning family of Holland. Beyond these signs of his activity, however, which I merely shared with all the readers of the daily press, I knew little of my former friend and companion.

One night – it was on the 20th of March, 1888 – I was returning from a journey to a patient (for I had now returned to civil practice), when my way led me through Baker Street. As I passed the well-remembered door, which must always be associated in my mind with my wooing, and with the dark incidents of the Study in Scarlet, I was seized with a keen desire to see Holmes again, and to know how he was employing his extraordinary powers. His rooms were brilliantly lit, and, even as I looked up, I saw his tall spare figure pass twice in a dark silhouette against the blind. He was pacing the room swiftly, eagerly, with his head sunk upon his chest, and his hands clasped behind him. To me, who knew his every mood and habit, his attitude and manner told their own story. He was at work again. He had risen out of his drug-created dreams, and was hot upon the scent of some new problem. I

master of his own establishment: owner of
   his own home
Bohemian: unconventional
cocaine: an addictive drug obtained from
   the leaves of the coca plant
singular: peculiar, strange
civil practice: Watson is now a GP
   (General Practitioner)
silhouette: shadowed outline
hot upon the scent: in active pursuit of, like
   a dog trailing its prey

COMMENTARY
Watson describes how he has seen little of Holmes since he married and left the lodgings which he and Holmes used to share together. One night, on his way back from seeing a patient, he passes Holmes's door and decides to call in.

rang the bell, and was shown up to the chamber which had formerly been in part my own.

His manner was not effusive. It seldom was; but he was glad, I think, to see me. With hardly a word spoken, but with a kindly eye, he waved me to an armchair, threw across his case of cigars, and indicated a spirit case and a gasogene in the corner. Then he stood before the fire, and looked me over in his singular introspective fashion.

'Wedlock suits you,' he remarked. 'I think, Watson, that you have put on seven and a half pounds since I saw you.'

'Seven,' I answered.

'Indeed, I should have thought a little more. Just a trifle more, I fancy, Watson. And in practice again, I observe. You did not tell me that you intended to go into harness.'

'Then, how do you know?'

'I see it, I deduce it. How do I know that you have been getting yourself very wet lately, and that you have a most clumsy and careless servant girl.'

'My dear Holmes,' said I, 'this is too much. You would certainly have been burned had you lived a few centuries ago. It is true that I had a country walk on Thursday and came home in a dreadful mess; but, as I have changed my clothes, I can't imagine how you deduce it. As to Mary Jane, she is incorrigible, and my wife has given her notice; but there again I fail to see how you work it out.'

He chuckled to himself and rubbed his long nervous hands together.

'It is simplicity itself,' said he; 'my eyes tell me that on the inside of your left shoe, just where the firelight strikes it, the leather is scored by six almost parallel cuts. Obviously they have been caused by someone who has very carelessly scraped round the edges of the sole in order to remove crusted mud from it. Hence, you see, my double deduction that you had been out in vile weather, and that you had a particularly malignant boot-slitting specimen of the London slavey. As to your practice, if a gentleman walks into my rooms smelling of iodoform, with a black mark of nitrate of silver upon his right

COMMENTARY

Holmes welcomes Watson in, and makes some deductions about his current lifestyle which astonish Watson by their accuracy. He explains how he has reached his conclusions.

effusive: gushing, readily showing his feelings

gasogene: apparatus for making soda-water

introspective: self-contained, inward-looking

go into harness: go to work

incorrigible: cannot be corrected

given her notice: told her that she will no longer be employed

malignant: wicked, harmful

slavey: most junior of household servants, maid-of-all-work

iodoform: a compound of iodine used as a medicine and as an antiseptic

nitrate of silver: a salt produced by the combination of nitric acid and silver, used as medicine

fore-finger, and a bulge on the side of his top hat to show where he has secreted his stethoscope, I must be dull indeed if I do not pronounce him to be an active member of the medical profession.'

I could not help laughing at the ease with which he explained his process of deduction. 'When I hear you give your reasons,' I remarked, 'the thing always appears to me to be so ridiculously simple that I could easily do it myself, though at each successive instance of your reasoning I am baffled, until you explain your process. And yet I believe that my eyes are as good as yours.'

'Quite so,' he answered, lighting a cigarette, and throwing himself down into an armchair. 'You see, but you do not observe. The distinction is clear. For example, you have frequently seen the steps which lead up from the hall to this room.'

'Frequently.'

'How often?'

'Well, some hundreds of times.'

'Then how many are there?'

'How many! I don't know.'

'Quite so. You have not observed. And yet you have seen. That is just my point. Now, I know that there are seventeen steps, because I have both seen and observed. By the way, since you are interested in these little problems, and since you are good enough to chronicle one or two of my trifling experiences, you may be interested in this.' He threw over a sheet of thick, pink-tinted note-paper which had been lying open upon the table. 'It came by the last post,' said he. 'Read it aloud.'

The note was undated, and without either signature or address.

'There will call upon you tonight, at a quarter to eight o'clock,' it said, 'a gentleman who desires to consult you upon a matter of the very deepest moment. Your recent services to one of the Royal Houses of Europe have shown that you are one who may safely be trusted with matters which are of an importance which can hardly be exaggerated. This account of you we have

---

trifling: trivial
of the very deepest moment: of the greatest importance

COMMENTARY
Holmes tells Watson of the important difference between 'seeing' and 'observing'. He also tells Watson of the latest case he is working on.

from all quarters received. Be in your chamber then at that hour, and do not take it amiss if your visitor wear a mask.'

'This is indeed a mystery,' I remarked. 'What do you imagine that it means?'

'I have no data yet. It is a capital mistake to theorise before one has data. Insensibly one begins to twist facts to suit theories, instead of theories to suit facts. But the note itself. What do you deduce from it?'

I carefully examined the writing, and the paper upon which it was written.

'The man who wrote it was presumably well-to-do,' I remarked, endeavouring to imitate my companion's processes. 'Such paper could not be bought under half-a-crown a packet. It is peculiarly strong and stiff.'

'Peculiar – that is the very word,' said Holmes. 'It is not an English paper at all. Hold it up to the light.'

I did so, and saw a large *E* with a small *g*, a *P*, and a large *G* with a small *t* woven into the texture of the paper.

'What do you make of that?' asked Holmes.

'The name of the maker, no doubt; or his monogram, rather.'

'Not at all. The *G* with the small *t* stands for "Gesellschaft", which is the German for "Company". It is a customary contraction like our "Co.". *P*, of course, stands for "Papier". Now for the *Eg*. Let us glance at our Continental Gazetteer.' He took down a heavy brown volume from his shelves. 'Eglow, Eglonitz – here we are, Egria. It is in a German-speaking country – in Bohemia, not far from Carlsbad. "Remarkable as being the scene of the death of Wallenstein, and for its numerous glass factories and paper mills." Ha, ha, my boy, what do you make of that?' His eyes sparkled, and he sent up a great blue triumphant cloud from his cigarette.

'The paper was made in Bohemia,' I said.

'Precisely. And the man who wrote the note is a German. Do you note the peculiar construction of the sentence – "This account of you we have from all quarters received". A Frenchman or Russian could not have written that. It is

COMMENTARY

Holmes invites his old friend to look at a letter he has been sent, and to draw some conclusions from it.

from all quarters: from everybody

capital: fatal

Insensibly: gradually, without being aware of it

Continental Gazetteer: a reference book giving facts about places on the continent of Europe

the German who is so uncourteous to his verbs. It only remains, therefore, to discover what is wanted by this German who writes upon Bohemian paper, and prefers wearing a mask to showing his face. And here he comes, if I am not mistaken, to resolve all our doubts.'

As he spoke there was the sharp sound of horses' hoofs and grating wheels against the kerb, followed by a sharp pull at the bell. Holmes whistled.

'A pair, by the sound,' said he. 'Yes,' he continued, glancing out of the window. 'A nice little brougham and a pair of beauties. A hundred and fifty guineas apiece. There's money in this case, Watson, if there is nothing else.'

'I think that I had better go, Holmes.'

'Not a bit, Doctor. Stay where you are. I am lost without my Boswell. And this promises to be interesting. It would be a pity to miss it.'

'But your client—'

'Never mind him. I may want your help, and so may he. Here he comes. Sit down in that armchair, Doctor, and give us your best attention.'

A slow and heavy step, which had been heard upon the stairs and in the passage, paused immediately outside the door. Then there was a loud and authoritative tap.

'Come in!' said Holmes.

A man entered who could hardly have been less than six feet six inches in height, with the chest and limbs of a Hercules. His dress was rich with a richness which would, in England, be looked upon as akin to bad taste. Heavy bands of astrakhan were slashed across the sleeves and fronts of his double-breasted coat, while the deep blue cloak which was thrown over his shoulders was lined with flame-coloured silk, and secured at the neck with a brooch which consisted of a single flaming beryl. Boots which extended half-way up his calves, and which were trimmed at the tops with a rich brown fur, completed the impression of barbaric opulence which was suggested by his whole appearance. He carried a broad-brimmed hat in his hand, while he wore across the upper part of his face, extending down past the cheek-bones, a black vizard mask, which he had apparently adjusted that moment, for his hand was

COMMENTARY
Holmes explains how he has worked out that the letter comes from a wealthy German-speaking client. At that moment, the client's carriage arrives. He is shown into Holmes's room.

uncourteous to: careless about
brougham: a horse-drawn carriage
guineas: one pound and one shilling
Boswell: a famous writer who recorded the thoughts and actions of his friend, Dr Samuel Johnson
authoritative: self-confident

Hercules: an Ancient Greek hero, famous for his great size and strength
astrakhan: a kind of fur
beryl: a semi-precious stone
barbaric opulence: a richly overdressed person
vizard mask: a mask covering the upper part of his face

still raised to it as he entered. From the lower part of the face he appeared to be a man of strong character, with a thick, hanging lip, and a long straight chin, suggestive of resolution pushed to the length of obstinacy.

'You had my note?' he asked, with a deep, harsh voice and a strongly marked German accent. 'I told you that I would call.' He looked from one to the other of us, as if uncertain which of us to address.

'Pray take a seat,' said Holmes. 'This is my friend and colleague, Dr Watson, who is occasionally good enough to help me in my cases. Whom have I the honour to address?'

'You may address me as the Count von Kramm, a Bohemian nobleman. I understand that this gentleman, your friend, is a man of honour and discretion, whom I may trust with a matter of the most extreme importance. If not, I should much prefer to communicate with you alone.'

I rose to go, but Holmes caught me by the wrist and pushed me back into my chair. 'It is both, or none,' said he. 'You may say before this gentleman anything which you may say to me.'

The Count shrugged his broad shoulders. 'Then I must begin,' said he, 'by binding you both to absolute secrecy for two years, at the end of that time the matter will be of no importance. At present it is not too much to say that it is of such weight that it may have an influence upon European history.'

'I promise,' said Holmes.

'And I.'

'You will excuse this mask,' continued our strange visitor. 'The august person who employs me wishes his agent to be unknown to you, and I may confess at once that the title by which I have just called myself is not exactly my own.'

'I was aware of it,' said Holmes dryly.

'The circumstances are of great delicacy, and every precaution has to be taken to quench what might grow to be an immense scandal and seriously compromise one of the reigning families of Europe. To speak plainly, the matter implicates the great House of Ormstein, hereditary kings of Bohemia.'

COMMENTARY

The Client, a man, is tall, showily dressed and talks with a German accent. He introduces himself as Count von Kramm. He is at first reluctant to discuss his problem in front of Dr Watson, but Holmes insists that Watson is entirely trustworthy. The Count explains why he is wearing a mask.

resolution: decisiveness
a man of honour: someone who will behave honourably
discretion: trustworthiness
weight: extreme seriousness
august: famous, distinguished
agent: someone acting on behalf of somebody else
quench: put an end to
scandal: a shocking fact
compromise: dishonour
implicates: concerns, involves

'I was also aware of that,' murmured Holmes, settling himself down in his armchair, and closing his eyes.

Our visitor glanced with some apparent surprise at the languid, lounging figure of the man who had been no doubt depicted to him as the most incisive reasoner, and most energetic agent in Europe. Holmes slowly reopened his eyes, and looked impatiently at his gigantic client.

'If your Majesty would condescend to state your case,' he remarked, 'I should be better able to advise you.'

The man sprang from his chair, and paced up and down the room in uncontrollable agitation. Then, with a gesture of desperation, he tore the mask from his face and hurled it upon the ground. 'You are right,' he cried, 'I am the King. Why should I attempt to conceal it?'

'Why, indeed?' murmured Holmes. 'Your Majesty had not spoken before I was aware that I was addressing Wilhelm Gottsreich Sigismond von Ormstein, Grand Duke of Cassel-Felstein, and hereditary King of Bohemia.'

'But you can understand,' said our strange visitor, sitting down once more and passing his hand over his high, white forehead, 'you can understand that I am not accustomed to doing such business in my own person. Yet the matter was so delicate that I could not confide it to an agent without putting myself in his power. I have come incognito from Prague for the purpose of consulting you.'

'Then, pray consult,' said Holmes, shutting his eyes once more.

'The facts are briefly these: Some five years ago, during a lengthy visit to Warsaw, I made the acquaintance of the well-known adventuress Irene Adler. The name is no doubt familiar to you.'

'Kindly look her up in my index, Doctor,' murmured Holmes, without opening his eyes. For many years he had adopted a system of docketing all paragraphs concerning men and things, so that it was difficult to name a subject or a person on which he could not at once furnish information. In this case I found her biography sandwiched in between that of a Hebrew Rabbi and that of a staff-commander who had written a monograph upon the deepsea fishes.

languid: showing only faint interest
incisive: sharp, intelligent
incognito: secretly, in disguise
adventuress: a woman seeking to make
    money out of somebody else
docketing: filing
monograph: a short booklet

COMMENTARY
Holmes reveals that he has deduced the true identity of his caller, and that he is none other than the King of Bohemia himself. The King explains that he has been involved in a love-affair with a singer called Irene Adler.

'Let me see,' said Holmes. 'Hum! Born in New Jersey in the year 1858. Contralto – hum! La Scala, hum! Prima donna Imperial Opera of Warsaw – Yes! Retired from operatic stage – ha! Living in London – quite so! Your Majesty, as I understand, became entangled with this young person, wrote her some compromising letters, and is now desirous of getting those letters back.'

'Precisely so. But how—'

'Was there a secret marriage?'

'None.'

'No legal papers or certificates?'

'None.'

'Then I fail to follow your Majesty. If this young person should produce her letters for blackmailing or other purposes, how is she to prove their authenticity?'

'There is the writing.'

'Pooh, pooh! Forgery.'

'My private note-paper.'

'Stolen.'

'My own seal.'

'Imitated.'

'My photograph.'

'Bought.'

'We were both in the photograph.'

'Oh, dear! That is very bad! Your Majesty has indeed committed an indiscretion.'

'I was mad – insane.'

'You have compromised yourself seriously.'

'I was only Crown Prince then. I was young. I am but thirty now.'

'It must be recovered.'

'We have tried and failed.'

'Your Majesty must pay. It must be bought.'

'She will not sell.'

COMMENTARY

The King wishes to keep his love-affair secret, but there is a photograph in which he and Irene appear together. This could ruin him completely.

Contralto: a female singer with a low singing voice

La Scala: an opera house in Milan, Italy

Prima donna: the principal singer

prove their authenticity: prove that they are genuine

recovered: got back

'Stolen, then.'

'Five attempts have been made. Twice burglars in my pay ransacked her house. Once we diverted her luggage when she travelled. Twice she has been waylaid. There has been no result.'

'No sign of it?'

'Absolutely none.'

Holmes laughed. 'It is quite a pretty little problem,' said he.

'But a very serious one to me,' returned the King, reproachfully.

'Very, indeed. And what does she propose to do with the photograph?'

'To ruin me.'

'But how?'

'I am about to be married.'

'So I have heard.'

'To Clotilde Lothman von Saxe-Meningen, second daughter of the King of Scandinavia. You may know the strict principles of her family. She is herself the very soul of delicacy. A shadow of a doubt as to my conduct would bring the matter to an end.'

'And Irene Adler?'

'Threatens to send them the photograph. And she will do it. I know that she will do it. You do not know her, but she has a soul of steel. She has the face of the most beautiful of women, and the mind of the most resolute of men. Rather than I should marry another woman, there are no lengths to which she would not go – none.'

'You are sure that she has not sent it yet?'

'I am sure.'

'And why?'

'Because she has said that she would send it on the day when the betrothal was publicly proclaimed. That will be next Monday.'

'Oh, then, we have three days yet,' said Holmes, with a yawn. 'That is very fortunate, as I have one or two matters of importance to look into just at present. Your Majesty will, of course, stay in London for the present?'

---

ransacked: burgled
reproachfully: disapprovingly
betrothal: promise to marry

COMMENTARY

Irene is threatening to make the photograph public on the day the King announces his engagement to the daughter of the King of Scandinavia. He is due to announce his engagement in three days' time, and asks Holmes to recover the photograph before then.

'Certainly. You will find me at the Langham, under the name of the Count von Kramm.'

'Then I shall drop you a line to let you know how we progress.

'Pray do so. I shall be all anxiety.'

'Then, as to money?'

'You have carte blanche.'

'Absolutely?'

'I tell you that I would give one of the provinces of my kingdom to have that photograph.'

'And for present expenses?'

The King took a heavy chamois leather bag from under his cloak, and laid it on the table.

'There are three hundred pounds in gold, and seven hundred in notes,' he said.

Holmes scribbled a receipt upon a sheet of his note-book, and handed it to him.

'And mademoiselle's address?' he asked.

'Is Briony Lodge, Serpentine Avenue, St John's Wood.'

Holmes took a note of it. 'One other question,' said he. 'Was the photograph a cabinet?'

'It was.'

'Then, good-night, your Majesty, and I trust that we shall soon have some good news for you. And good night, Watson,' he added, as the wheels of the Royal brougham rolled down the street. 'If you will be good enough to call tomorrow afternoon, at three o'clock, I should like to chat this little matter over with you.'

At three o'clock precisely I was at Baker Street, but Holmes had not yet returned. The landlady informed me that he had left the house shortly after eight o'clock in the morning. I sat down beside the fire, however, with the intention of awaiting him, however long he might be. I

COMMENTARY

The King leaves, saying he will pay anything to get the photograph back, and giving Holmes a large bag of gold to be getting on with. Holmes asks Watson to call in the following afternoon to discuss the case with him.

carte blanche: a free hand

chamois: soft, expensive leather

cabinet: a large, portrait-sized photograph in a heavy frame

was already deeply interested in his inquiry, for, though it was surrounded by none of the grim and strange features which were associated with the two crimes which I have elsewhere recorded, still, the nature of the case and the exalted station of his client gave it a character of its own. Indeed, apart from the nature of the investigation which my friend had on hand, there was something in his masterly grasp of a situation, and his keen incisive reasoning, which made it a pleasure to me to study his system of work, and to follow the quick, subtle methods by which he disentangled the most inextricable mysteries. So accustomed was I to his invariable success, that the very possibility of his failing had ceased to enter into my head.

It was close upon four before the door opened, and a drunken-looking groom, ill-kempt and side-whiskered with an inflamed face and disreputable clothes, walked into the room. Accustomed as I was to my friend's amazing powers in the use of disguises, I had to look three times before I was certain that it was indeed he. With a nod he vanished into the bedroom, whence he emerged in five minutes tweed-suited and respectable, as of old. Putting his hands into his pockets, he stretched out his legs in front of the fire, and laughed heartily for some minutes.

'Well, really' he cried, and then he choked; and laughed again until he was obliged to lie back, limp and helpless, in the chair.

'What is it?'

'It's quite too funny. I am sure you could never guess how I employed my morning, or what I ended by doing.'

'I can't imagine. I suppose that you have been watching the habits, and perhaps the house, of Miss Irene Adler.'

'Quite so, but the sequel was rather unusual. I will tell you, however. I left the house a little after eight o'clock this morning, in the character of a groom out of work. There is a wonderful sympathy and freemasonry among horsey men. Be one of them, and you will know all that there is to know. I soon found Briony Lodge. It is a *bijou* villa, with a garden at the back, but built out in front right up to the road, two stories. Chubb lock to the door. Large sitting-

---

exalted station: noble rank
subtle: skilful, clever
inextricable: involved, complicated
groom: someone who tends horses
sequel: episode which followed
character: disguise
freemasonry: fellow-feeling, comradeship
bijou villa: small elegant house

COMMENTARY
Holmes is not there when Watson arrives, but soon comes in, disguised as a groom. He changes his clothes and sits down in a chair, laughing. Watson asks him why he is so amused.

room on the right side, well-furnished, with long windows almost to the floor, and those preposterous English window fasteners which a child could open. Behind there was nothing remarkable, save that the passage window could be reached from the top of the coach-house. I walked round it and examined it closely from every point of view, but without noting anything else of interest.

'I then lounged down the street, and found, as I expected, that there was a mews in a lane which runs down by the wall of the garden. I lent the ostlers a hand in rubbing down their horses, and I received in exchange twopence, a glass of half-and-half, two fills of shag tobacco, and as much information as I could desire about Miss Adler, to say nothing of half a dozen people in the neighbourhood in whom I was not in the least interested, but whose biographies I was compelled to listen to.'

'And what of Irene Adler?'

'Oh, she has turned all the men's heads in that part. She is the daintiest thing under a bonnet on this planet. So say the Serpentine Mews to a man. She lives quietly, sings at concerts, drives out at five every day, and returns at seven sharp for dinner. Seldom goes out at other times, except when she sings. Has only one male visitor, but a good deal of him. He is dark, handsome, and dashing; never calls less than once a day, and often twice. He is a Mr Godfrey Norton, of the Inner Temple. See the advantages of a cabman as a confidant. They had driven him home a dozen times from Serpentine Mews, and knew all about him. When I had listened to all that they had to tell, I began to walk up and down near Briony Lodge once more, and to think over my plan of campaign.

'This Godfrey Norton was evidently an important factor in the matter. He was a lawyer. That sounded ominous. What was the relation between them, and what the object of his repeated visits? Was she his client, his friend, or his mistress? If the former, she had probably transferred the photograph to his keeping. If the latter, it was less likely. On the issue of this question depended whether I should continue my work at Briony Lodge, or turn my attentions to the gentleman's chambers in the Temple. It was a

COMMENTARY

Holmes tells Watson of his day spent finding out about Irene Adler, talking to the men who work in the street where she lives. He has learned that she is very pretty and very popular.

It appears that Irene leads a very quiet social life, apart from having one regular male visitor, a lawyer called Godfrey Norton. Holmes is concerned to find out what their relationship is, as it will affect Irene 's behaviour and the chances of recovering the photograph.

preposterous: ridiculous
ostlers: people who look after horses
half-and-half: a mixture of mud and bitter beer
biographies: life histories
the daintiest thing under a bonnet: prettiest woman
to a man: every man without exception
dashing: lively
ominous: a bad thing, unfortunate
chambers: rooms

delicate point, and it widened the field of my inquiry. I fear that I bore you with these details, but I have to let you see my little difficulties, if you are to understand the situation.'

'I am following you closely,' I answered.

'I was still balancing the matter in my mind when a hansom cab drove up to Briony Lodge, and a gentleman sprang out. He was a remarkably handsome man, dark, aquiline, and moustached – evidently the man of whom I had heard. He appeared to be in a great hurry, shouted to the cabman to wait, and brushed past the maid who opened the door with the air of a man who was thoroughly at home.

'He was in the house about half an hour, and I could catch glimpses of him, in the windows of the sitting-room, pacing up and down, talking excitedly and waving his arms. Of her I could see nothing. Presently he emerged, looking even more flurried than before. As he stepped up to the cab, he pulled a gold watch from his pocket and looked at it earnestly, "Drive like the devil," he shouted, "first to Gross and Hankey's in Regent Street, and then to the church of St Monica in the Edgware Road. Half a guinea if you do it in twenty minutes!"

'Away they went, and I was just wondering whether I should not do well to follow them, when up the lane came a neat little landau, the coachman with his coat only half buttoned, while all the tags of his harness were sticking out of their buckles. It hadn't pulled up before she shot out of the hall door and into it. I only caught a glimpse of her at the moment, but she was a lovely woman, with a face a man might die for.

'"The Church of St Monica, John," she cried, 'and half a sovereign if you reach it in twenty minutes."

'This was quite too good to lose, Watson. I was just balancing whether I should run for it, or whether I should perch behind her landau, when a cab came through the street. The driver looked twice at such a shabby fare; but I jumped in before he could object. "The Church of St Monica," said I, "and half a sovereign if you reach it in twenty minutes." It was twenty-five minutes

hansom cab: a small horse-drawn carriage
   for two people
aquiline: with a narrow, pointed face
flurried: agitated
Gross and Hankey's: a jeweller's
landau: a four-wheeled carriage
sovereign: a gold coin worth one pound
balancing: weighing up

COMMENTARY

As Holmes, outside Irene's house, is deciding on his plan of action, Godfrey Norton arrives. He goes in and talks to Irene in an agitated way. Norton comes out of the house and jumps into a cab, telling it to go first to a jeweller's and then to a church. Next Irene comes out, gets into *her* carriage and makes off at speed for the church.

to twelve, and of course it was clear enough what was in the wind.

'My cabby drove fast. I don't think I ever drove faster, but the others were there before us. The cab and the landau with their steaming horses were in front of the door when I arrived. I paid the man, and hurried into the church. There was not a soul there save the two whom I had followed, and a surpliced clergyman, who seemed to be expostulating with them. They were all three standing in a knot in front of the altar. I lounged up the side aisle like any other idler who has dropped into a church. Suddenly, to my surprise, the three at the altar faced round to me, and Godfrey Norton came running as hard as he could towards me.

'"Thank God!" he cried. "You'll do. Come! Come!"

'"What then?" I asked.

'"Come, man, come, only three minutes or it won't be legal."

'I was half dragged up to the altar, and before I knew where I was, I found myself mumbling responses which were whispered in my ear, and vouching for things of which I knew nothing, and generally assisting in the secure tying up of Irene Adler, spinster, to Godfrey Norton, bachelor. It was all done in an instant, and there was the gentleman thanking me on the one side, and the lady on the other, while the clergyman beamed on me in front. It was the most preposterous position in which I ever found myself in my life, and it was the thought of it that started me laughing just now. It seems that there had been some informality about their licence, that the clergyman absolutely refused to marry them without a witness of some sort, and that my lucky appearance saved the bridegroom from having to sally out into the streets in search of a best man. The bride gave me a sovereign, and I mean to wear it on my watch-chain in memory of the occasion.'

'This is a very unexpected turn of affairs,' said I, 'and what then?'

'Well, I found my plan very seriously menaced. It looked as if the pair might take an immediate departure, and so necessitate very prompt and energetic measures on my part. At the church door, however, they separated,

COMMENTARY

Holmes follows in another cab, and arrives at the church to find the couple in urgent conversation with a priest. Godfrey Norton sees Holmes lurking at the back of the church, and drags him up to the altar to act as witness at his marriage to Irene. The couple then leave the church and go their separate ways, arranging to meet later on in the day.

what was in the wind: what was happening

surpliced: wearing a surplice, a loose robe of white linen with wide sleeves

expostulating: arguing

tying up: marrying

some informality: something out of order

licence: formal written permission, without which the marriage would be illegal

sally: wander

menaced: threatened

he driving back to the Temple, and she to her own house. "I shall drive out in the Park at five as usual," she said as she left him. I heard no more. They drove away in different directions, and I went off to make my own arrangements.'

'Which are?'

'Some cold beef and a glass of beer,' he answered, ringing the bell. 'I have been too busy to think of food, and I am likely to be busier still this evening. By the way, Doctor, I shall want your co-operation.

Look out for...
- **the way in which Holmes sets up the afternoon's events.**
- **Watson's gradual understanding of what is going on.**
- **the suggestion that Holmes has not been as clever as he thinks.**

'I shall be delighted.'

'You don't mind breaking the law?'

'Not in the least.'

'Nor running a chance of arrest?'

'Not in a good cause.'

'Oh, the cause is excellent!'

'Then I am your man.'

'I was sure that I might rely on you.'

'But what is it you wish?'

'When Mrs Turner has brought in the tray I will make it clear to you. Now,' he said, as he turned hungrily on the simple fare that our landlady had provided, 'I must discuss it while I eat, for I have not much time. It is nearly five now. In two hours we must be on the scene of action. Miss Irene, or Madame, rather, returns from her drive at seven. We must be at Briony Lodge to meet her.'

Mrs Turner: Holmes's housekeeper
fare: food

COMMENTARY
Holmes enlists Watson's help in his plan to find out where Irene Adler has hidden the photograph.

'And what then?'

'You must leave that to me. I have already arranged what is to occur. There is only one point on which I must insist. You must not interfere, come what may. You understand?'

'I am to be neutral?'

'To do nothing whatever. There will probably be some small unpleasantness. Do not join in it. It will end in my being conveyed into the house. Four or five minutes afterwards the sitting-room window will open. You are to station yourself close to that open window.'

'Yes.'

'You are to watch me, for I will be visible to you.'

'Yes.'

'And when I raise my hand – so – you will throw into the room what I give you to throw, and will, at the same time, raise the cry of fire. You quite follow me?'

'Entirely.'

'It is nothing very formidable,' he said, taking a long cigar-shaped roll from his pocket. 'It is an ordinary plumber's smoke rocket, fitted with a cap at either end to make it self-lighting. Your task is confined to that. When you raise your cry of fire, it will be taken up by quite a number of people. You may then walk to the end of the street, and I will rejoin you in ten minutes. I hope that I have made myself clear?'

'I am to remain neutral, to get near the window, to watch you, and, at the signal, to throw in this object, then to raise the cry of fire, and to await you at the corner of the street.'

'Precisely.'

'Then you may entirely rely on me.'

'That is excellent. I think perhaps it is almost time that I prepared for the new *rôle* I have to play.'

COMMENTARY

Holmes explains to Watson exactly what he wants him to do. Watson is to throw a smoke rocket into Irene's house, so that she will think it is on fire. He is then to wait for Holmes. Watson agrees to do as Holmes asks.

conveyed: carried

station yourself: stand

I will be visible to you: you will be able to see me

formidable: amazing

plumber's smoke rocket: a device used by plumbers to check the seals on joints in pipework by releasing smoke through the pipe

confined: limited

PAUSE FOR PLAYBACK:
Now look at the playback questions on page 35 before going on with
your reading.

He disappeared into his bedroom, and returned in a few minutes in the
character of an amiable and simple-minded Non-conformist clergyman. His
broad black hat, his baggy trousers, his white tie, his sympathetic smile, and
general look of peering and benevolent curiosity, were such as Mr John Hare
alone could have equalled. It was not merely that Holmes changed his
costume. His expression, his manner, his very soul seemed to vary with every
fresh part that he assumed. The stage lost a fine actor, even as science lost an
acute reasoner, when he became a specialist in crime.

It was a quarter past six when we left Baker Street, and it still wanted ten
minutes to the hour when we found ourselves in Serpentine Avenue. It was
already dusk, and the lamps were just being lighted as we paced up and down
in front of Briony Lodge, waiting for the coming of its occupant. The house
was just such as I had pictured it from Sherlock Holmes's succinct description,
but the locality appeared to be less private than I expected. On the contrary,
for a small street in a quiet neighbourhood, it was remarkably animated. There
was a group of shabbily dressed men smoking and laughing in a corner, a
scissors-grinder with his wheel, two guardsmen who were flirting with a nurse-
girl, and several well-dressed young men who were lounging up and down with
cigars in their mouths.

'You see,' remarked Holmes, as we paced to and fro in front of the house,
'this marriage rather simplifies matters. The photograph becomes a double-
edged weapon now. The chances are that she would be as averse to its being
seen by Mr Godfrey Norton, as our client is to its coming to the eyes of his
Princess. Now the question is – Where are we to find the photograph?'

Non-conformist clergyman: a Protestant
   priest who is not a member of the
   Church of England
benevolent: kindly
Mr John Hare: a famous actor of the time
succinct: brief and concise
averse: opposed

COMMENTARY
Holmes disguises himself as a
clergyman and he and Watson set off
for Irene's house.

'Where, indeed?'

'It is most unlikely that she carries it about with her. It is cabinet size. Too large for easy concealment about a woman's dress. She knows that the King is capable of having her waylaid and searched. Two attempts of the sort have already been made. We may take it then that she does not carry it about with her.'

'Where, then?'

'Her banker or her lawyer. There is that double possibility. But I am inclined to think neither. Women are naturally secretive, and they like to do their own secreting. Why should she hand it over to anyone else? She could trust her own guardianship, but she could not tell what indirect or political influence might be brought to bear upon a business man. Besides, remember that she had resolved to use it within a few days. It must be where she can lay her hands upon it. It must be in her own house.'

'But it has twice been burgled.'

'Pshaw! They did not know how to look.'

'But how will you look?'

'I will not look.'

'What then?'

'I will get her to show me.'

'But she will refuse.'

'She will not be able to. But I hear the rumble of wheels. It is her carriage. Now carry out my orders to the letter.'

As he spoke, the gleam of the sidelights of a carriage came round the curve of the avenue. It was a smart little landau which rattled up to the door of Briony Lodge. As it pulled up, one of the loafing men at the corner dashed forward to open the door in the hope of earning a copper, but was elbowed away by another loafer who had rushed up with the same intention. A fierce quarrel broke out, which was increased by the two guardsmen, who took sides with one of the loungers, and by the scissors-grinder, who was equally hot upon the other side. A blow was struck, and in an instant the lady, who had stepped from her carriage, was the centre of a little knot of flushed and

COMMENTARY

Holmes tells Watson he is confident that Irene has the photograph hidden in her house, somewhere where she can get at it easily, and where her new husband will not find it. He says that he will get Irene to show him where the photograph is kept. Just then, the lady herself returns in her carriage. As she is stepping out, a fight occurs between two men in the street, putting her at risk.

waylaid: attacked, ambushed
resolved: made up her mind
loafing: idling, hanging about
copper: old penny

struggling men who struck savagely at each other with their fists and sticks. Holmes dashed into the crowd to protect the lady; but just as he reached her, he gave a cry and dropped to the ground, with the blood running freely down his face. At his fall the guardsmen took to their heels in one direction and the loungers in the other, while a number of better dressed people who had watched the scuffle without taking part in it, crowded in to help the lady and to attend to the injured man. Irene Adler, as I will still call her, had hurried up the steps; but she stood at the top with her superb figure outlined against the lights of the hall, looking back into the street.

'Is the poor gentleman much hurt?' she asked.

'He is dead,' cried several voices.

'No, no, there's life in him,' shouted another. 'But he'll be gone before you can get him to hospital.'

'He's a brave fellow,' said a woman. 'They would have had the lady's purse and watch if it hadn't been for him. They were a gang, and a rough one, too. Ah, he's breathing now.'

'He can't lie in the street. May we bring him in, marm?'

'Surely. Bring him into the sitting-room. There is a comfortable sofa. This way, please!'

Slowly and solemnly he was borne into Briony Lodge, and laid out in the principal room, while I still observed the proceedings from my post by the window. The lamps had been lit, but the blinds had not been drawn, so that I could see Holmes as he lay upon the couch. I do not know whether he was seized with compunction at that moment for the part he was playing, but I know that I never felt more heartily ashamed of myself in my life than when I saw the beautiful creature against whom I was conspiring, or the grace and kindliness with which she waited upon the injured man. And yet it would be the blackest treachery to Holmes to draw back now from the part which he had entrusted to me. I hardened my heart and took the smoke-rocket from under my ulster. After all, I thought, we are not injuring her. We are but preventing her from injuring another.

marm: madam
borne: carried
principal: main
compunction: an uneasy conscience
ulster: a type of overcoat

COMMENTARY
Holmes goes to protect Irene and is knocked down. He appears to be badly hurt. He is carried into the house.

Holmes had sat up upon the couch, and I saw him motion like a man who is in want of air. A maid rushed across and threw open the window. At the same instant I saw him raise his hand, and at the signal I tossed my rocket into the room with a cry of 'Fire'. The word was no sooner out of my mouth than the whole crowd of spectators, well dressed and ill – gentlemen, ostlers, and servant maids – joined in a general shriek of 'Fire'. Thick clouds of smoke curled into the room, and out at the open window. I caught a glimpse of rushing figures, and a moment later the voice of Holmes from within, assuring them that it was a false alarm. Slipping through the shouting crowd I made my way to the corner of the street, and in ten minutes was rejoiced to find my friend's arm in mine, and to get away from the scene of the uproar. He walked swiftly and in silence for some few minutes, until we had turned down one of the quiet streets which lead towards the Edgware Road.

'You did it very nicely, Doctor,' he remarked. 'Nothing could have been better. It is all right.'

'You have the photograph!'

'I know where it is.'

'And how did you find out?'

'She showed me, as I told you she would.'

'I am still in the dark.'

'I do not wish to make a mystery,' said he, laughing. 'The matter was perfectly simple. You, of course, saw that everyone in the street was an accomplice. They were all engaged for the evening.'

'I guessed as much.'

'Then, when the row broke out, I had a little moist red paint in the palm of my hand. I rushed forward, fell down, clapped my hand to my face, and became a piteous spectacle. It is an old trick.'

'That also I could fathom.'

'Then they carried me in. She was bound to have me in. What else could she do? And into her sitting-room which was the very room which I suspected. It lay between that and her bedroom, and I was determined to see which. They

COMMENTARY

Watson waits for Holmes's signal and then throws in the smoke rocket. He walks away from the scene and is joined a few minutes later by Holmes. They walk away together. Holmes explains to Watson that the fight was a put-up job in order that he might get into the house.

rejoiced: happy and relieved
in the dark: bewildered
accomplice: in on the plot
engaged: hired (by Holmes)
fathom: work out

laid me on a couch, I motioned for air, they were compelled to open the window, and you had your chance.'

'How did that help you?'

'It was all-important. When a woman thinks that her house is on fire, her instinct is at once to rush to the thing which she values most. It is a perfectly overpowering impulse, and I have more than once taken advantage of it. In the case of the Darlington Substitution Scandal it was of use to me, and also in the Arnsworth Castle business. A married woman grabs at her baby, an unmarried one reaches for her jewel box. Now it was clear to me that our lady of to-day had nothing in the house more precious to her than what we are in quest of. She would rush to secure it. The alarm of fire was admirably done. The smoke and shouting was enough to shake nerves of steel. She responded beautifully. The photograph is in a recess behind a sliding panel just above the right bell-pull. She was there in an instant, and I caught a glimpse of it as she half drew it out. When I cried out that it was a false alarm, she replaced it, glanced at the rocket, rushed from the room, and I have not seen her since. I rose, and, making my excuses, escaped from the house. I hesitated whether to attempt to secure the photograph at once; but the coachman had come in, and as he was watching me narrowly, it seemed safer to wait. A little over-precipitance may ruin all.'

'And now?' I asked.

'Our quest is practically finished. I shall call with the King tomorrow, and with you, if you care to come with us. We will be shown into the sitting-room to wait for the lady, but it is probable that when she comes she may find neither us nor the photograph. It might be a satisfaction to His Majesty to regain it with his own hands.'

'And when will you call?'

'At eight in the morning. She will not be up, so that we shall have a clear field. Besides, we must be prompt, for this marriage may mean a complete change in her life and habits. I must wire to the King without delay.'

We had reached Baker Street, and had stopped at the door. He was searching his pockets for the key, when some one passing said:

quest: search
over-precipitance: haste
wire to: send a telegraph message

COMMENTARY
When the fire alarm was raised, Holmes was able to see Irene checking that the photograph was still safe. Holmes confirms that he now knows where the photograph is hidden and that he plans to go back to the house the next day with the King in order to retrieve it.

'Good night, Mister Sherlock Holmes.'

There were several people on the pavement at the time, but the greeting appeared to come from a slim youth in an ulster who had hurried by.

'I've heard that voice before,' said Holmes, staring down the dimly lit street. 'Now, I wonder who the deuce that could have been.'

I slept at Baker Street that night, and we were engaged upon our toast and coffee when the King of Bohemia rushed into the room.

'You have really got it!' he cried, grasping Sherlock Holmes by either shoulder, and looking eagerly into his face.

'Not yet.'

'But you have hopes?'

'I have hopes.'

'Then, come. I am all impatience to be gone.'

'We must have a cab.'

'No, my brougham is waiting.'

'Then that will simplify matters.'

We descended, and started off once more for Briony Lodge.

'Irene Adler is married,' remarked Holmes.

'Married! When?'

'Yesterday.'

'But to whom?'

'To an English lawyer named Norton.'

'But she could not love him?'

'I am in hopes that she does.'

'And why in hopes?'

'Because it would spare your Majesty all fear of future annoyance. If the lady loves her husband, she does not love your Majesty. If she does not love your Majesty there is no reason why she should interfere with your Majesty's plan.'

'It is true. And yet—! Well! I wish she had been of my own station! What a queen she would have made!' He relapsed into a moody silence which was

the deuce: the devil
I wish she had been of my own station: I wish she had been of my own social class
relapsed: fell back

not broken until we drew up in Serpentine Avenue.

The door of Briony Lodge was open, and an elderly woman stood upon the steps. She watched us with a *sardonic eye* as we stepped from the brougham.

'Mr Sherlock Holmes, I believe?' said she.

'I am Mr Holmes,' answered my companion, looking at her with a questioning and rather startled gaze.

'Indeed! My mistress told me that you were likely to call. She left this morning with her husband, by the 5.15 train from Charing Cross, for the Continent.'

'What!' Sherlock Holmes staggered back, white with *chagrin* and surprise. 'Do you mean that she has left England?'

'Never to return.'

'And the papers?' asked the King, hoarsely. 'All is lost.'

'We shall see.' He pushed past the servant, and rushed into the drawing-room, followed by the King and myself. The furniture was scattered about in every direction, with dismantled shelves, and open drawers, as if the lady had hurriedly ransacked them before her flight. Holmes rushed at the bell-pull, tore back a small sliding shutter, and, plunging in his hand, pulled out a photograph and a letter. The photograph was of Irene Adler herself in evening dress, the letter was *superscribed* to 'Sherlock Holmes, Esq. To be left till called for.' My friend tore it open and we all three read it together. It was dated at midnight of the preceding night, and ran in this way:

My Dear Mr Sherlock Holmes,

You really did it very well. You took me in completely. Until after the alarm of fire, I had not a suspicion. But then, when I found how I had betrayed myself, I began to think. I had been warned against you months ago. I had been told that if the King employed an agent, it would certainly be you. And your address had been given me. Yet, with all this, you made me reveal what you wanted to know. Even after I became suspicious, I found it hard to think evil of such a dear, kind old clergyman. But, you know, I have been trained as an actress myself. Male costume is nothing

sardonic eye: mocking look
chagrin: disappointed
superscribed: addressed

COMMENTARY
A woman meets them at the door of the house and tells them that Irene has left England. She gives Holmes an envelope addressed to him. He takes out a letter from Irene and reads it.

new to me. I often take advantage of the freedom which it gives. I sent John, the coachman, to watch you, ran upstairs, got into my walking clothes, as I call them, and came down just as you departed.

Well, I followed you to your door and so made sure that I was really an object of interest to the celebrated Mr Sherlock Holmes. Then I, rather imprudently, wished you good-night, and started for the Temple to see my husband.

We both thought the best resource was flight when pursued by so formidable an antagonist; so you will find the nest empty when you call to-morrow. As to the photograph, your client may rest in peace. I love and am loved by a better man than he. The King may do what he will without hindrance from one whom he has cruelly wronged. I keep it only to safeguard myself, and to preserve a weapon which will always secure me from any steps which he might take in the future. I leave a photograph which he might care to possess; and I remain, dear Mr Sherlock Holmes, very truly yours,

IRENE NORTON, *née* ADLER.

'What a woman – oh, what a woman!' cried the King of Bohemia, when we had all three read this epistle. 'Did I not tell you how quick and resolute she was? Would she not have made an admirable queen? Is it not a pity she was not on my level?'

'From what I have seen of the lady, she seems, indeed, to be on a very different level to your Majesty,' said Holmes, coldly. 'I am sorry that I have not been able to bring your Majesty's business to a more successful conclusion.'

'On the contrary, my dear sir,' cried the King. 'Nothing could be more successful. I know that her word is inviolate. The photograph is now as safe as if it were in the fire.'

'I am glad to hear your Majesty say so.'

'I am immensely indebted to you. Pray tell me in what way I can reward

COMMENTARY

Irene Adler's letter explains that she worked out the plot against her and followed Holmes and Watson in disguise. It was she who greeted Holmes in the street. She has now left England with her husband, taking the photograph with her, but promising never to use it against the King. The King says how much he regrets not having married her.

imprudently: unwisely
antagonist: enemy
not on my level: not of my social class
on a very different level: a very different and more impressive person
inviolate: totally trustworthy

you. This ring—' He slipped an emerald snake ring from his finger and held it out upon the palm of his hand.

'Your Majesty has something which I should value even more highly,' said Holmes.

'You have but to name it.'

'This photograph!'

The King stared at him in amazement.

'Irene's photograph!' he cried. 'Certainly, if you wish it.'

'I thank your Majesty. Then there is no more to be done in the matter. I have the honour to wish you a very good morning.' He bowed, and, turning away without observing the hand which the King stretched out to him, he set off in my company for his chambers.

And that was how a great scandal threatened to affect the kingdom of Bohemia, and how the best plans of Mr Sherlock Holmes were beaten by a woman's wit. He used to make merry over the cleverness of women, but I have not heard him do it of late. And when he speaks of Irene Adler, or when he refers to her photograph, it is always under the honourable title of *the* woman.

PAUSE FOR PLAYBACK:
Now look at the playback questions on page 35.

COMMENTARY

The King offers Holmes a valuable jewel as a reward, but Holmes says he would rather have the second photograph which Irene has left behind. Watson tells how Holmes's view of women has changed since his encounter with Irene Adler. He now regards them with much more respect, and has a particular admiration for one woman in particular.

Study guide

PLAYBACK QUESTIONS

PAGES 9 TO 25:

- ➤ What have you learned about Sherlock Holmes's methods of working as a detective?
- ➤ What impression have you formed of Irene Adler so far? Who will win the battle of wits between Irene and Holmes?
- ➤ What are we meant to make of the King of Bohemia? Will he get the result he wants at the end of the case?
- ➤ How is Holmes going to try to get the photograph back? Will it work?

Now return to reading the story on page 26

PAGES 26 TO 34:

- ➤ How does Holmes get into Irene's house? Why does he need to?
- ➤ Re-read Irene's letter on pages 32 and 33. How do you feel about what she has done?
- ➤ What are Holmes's feelings about being out-witted by Irene? Do you share them?
- ➤ Why is this story entitled *A Scandal in Bohemia*? Do you find it a suitable title, or can you think of a better one?

REVIEWING THE WHOLE STORY: SUGGESTED ACTIVITIES

1 Police investigation

There are four main characters in the story: Sherlock Holmes, Dr Watson, Irene Adler and the King of Bohemia.

Imagine that the police get to hear of the fight in the street and the false fire at Irene Adler's house. They decide to set up an investigation into everything that has been going on.

a **With a partner**, go through the whole story, picking out every detail you can find that gives you information about (i) what the four characters look like, (ii) where they live, and (iii) what sort of personalities they have. Working together, draw up a profile sheet for each character. You can devise your own sheet or use the one shown below as a model.

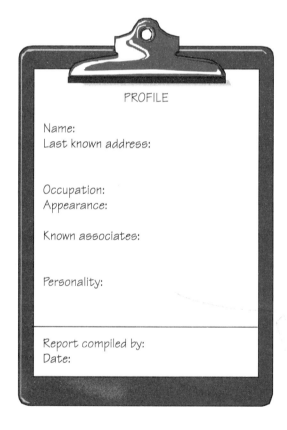

```
                    PROFILE

   Name:
   Last known address:


   Occupation:
   Appearance:

   Known associates:


   Personality:


   Report compiled by:
   Date:
```

b **By yourself**, write a police report about the events that took place outside and inside Irene Adler's house. Use a formal, Standard English style and make the report as clear, concise and well-organised as possible.

2 │ Irene Adler and the men in her life

When we are introduced to Irene Adler for the first time, we learn that she has had a relationship with the King of Bohemia. In the course of the story, we see her getting married to Godfrey Norton.

a   **As a class**, talk about what we are told of the two men in Irene's life. Make your own notes, together with page references, about the kind of characters they are and what might have attracted Irene to them.

b   **With a partner**, write down your notes in the form of character portraits of the King of Bohemia and Godfrey Norton. Your task is to describe *the kind of people they are* rather than just give an account of the part they played in the story.

c   **By yourself**, imagine that Irene Adler writes a letter to her new husband, to be given to him after they leave England. The letter tells him everything about her past life, her relationship with the King of Bohemia and her outwitting of Sherlock Holmes.

Write Irene's letter. Try to bring out as much about your understanding of her character as possible, both through what she says and the way in which she says it.

3 │ TV chat show

At the end of the story Sherlock Holmes refuses to shake the King's hand. *A Scandal in Bohemia* is also one of the very few cases in which Holmes is out-smarted by someone (Irene) he is employed to investigate.

Imagine that Sherlock Holmes, Irene Adler and the King of Bohemia accept invitations to appear on a TV chat show to talk about themselves, their relationships, and their feelings about each other now the case is over.

a   **In a group**, decide who will role-play each of the three chat show guests and who will be the host/hostess. Plan what you will say.

b   When your group feels sufficiently prepared, act out a scene from the chat show lasting between 5 and 10 minutes in which the guests are asked about what happened and how they feel about it.

Be prepared to show your scene to the rest of the class, and to answer questions about how you have planned and performed it.

THE SPECKLED BAND

Look out for...
- **Dr Grimesby Roylott. What kind of person is he, and how do we know?**
- **the way in which Sherlock Holmes is led astray by a false clue.**

In glancing over my notes of the seventy odd cases in which I have during the last eight years studied the methods of my friend Sherlock Holmes, I find many tragic, some comic, a large number merely strange, but none commonplace; for, working as he did rather for the love of his art than for the acquirement of wealth, he refused to associate himself with any investigation which did not tend towards the unusual, and even the fantastic. Of all these varied cases, however, I cannot recall any which presented more singular features than that which was associated with the well-known Surrey family of the Roylotts of Stoke Moran. The events in question occurred in the early days of my association with Holmes, when we were sharing rooms as bachelors, in Baker Street. It is possible that I might have placed them upon record before, but a promise of secrecy was made at the time, from which I have only been freed during the last month by the untimely death of the lady to whom the pledge was given. It is perhaps as well that the facts should now come to light, for I have reasons to know there are widespread rumours as to the death of Dr Grimesby Roylott which tend to make the matter even more terrible than the truth.

COMMENTARY

Doctor Watson remembers past cases in which he has been involved with Sherlock Holmes. He says that this one is among the most extraordinary he can remember. He was not able to write it down before, because of a promise he made to a woman involved in the story.

commonplace: ordinary
singular: extraordinary
bachelors: unmarried men
pledge: promise

It was early in April, in the year '83, that I woke one morning to find Sherlock Holmes standing, fully dressed, by the side of my bed. He was a late riser as a rule, and, as the clock on the mantelpiece showed me that it was only a quarter past seven, I blinked up at him in some surprise, and perhaps just a little resentment, for I was myself regular in my habits.

'Very sorry to knock you up, Watson,' said he, 'but it's the common lot this morning. Mrs Hudson has been knocked up, she retorted upon me, and I on you.'

'What is it, then? A fire?'

'No, a client. It seems that a young lady has arrived in a considerable state of excitement, who insists upon seeing me. She is waiting now in the sitting-room. Now, when young ladies wander about the metropolis at this hour of the morning, and knock sleepy people up out of their beds, I presume that it is something very pressing which they have to communicate. Should it prove to be an interesting case, you would, I am sure, wish to follow it from the outset. I thought at any rate that I should call you, and give you the chance.'

'My dear fellow, I would not miss it for anything.'

I had no keener pleasure than in following Holmes in his professional investigations, and in admiring the rapid deductions, as swift as intuitions, and yet always founded on a logical basis, with which he unravelled the problems which were submitted to him. I rapidly threw on my clothes, and was ready in a few minutes to accompany my friend down to the sitting-room. A lady dressed in black and heavily veiled, who had been sitting in the window, rose as we entered.

'Good morning, madam,' said Holmes, cheerily. 'My name is Sherlock Holmes. This is my intimate friend and associate, Dr Watson, before whom you can speak as freely as before myself. Ha, I am glad to see that Mrs Hudson has had the good sense to light the fire. Pray draw up to it, and I shall order you a cup of hot coffee, for I observe that you are shivering.'

'It is not cold which makes me shiver,' said the woman in a low voice, changing her seat as requested.

'What then?'

it's the common lot: it has happened to
  everyone
metropolis: city of London
pressing: urgent
intuitions: sudden understandings or
  'hunches'

COMMENTARY
The case begins when Holmes wakes Watson up early one morning to say that a young woman has called to consult him. They both go down to greet her.

[handwritten margin notes: prematurely grey; simile; take everything in; pats her arm; for sympathy; metaphor; pay you later when marriage]

'It is fear, Mr Holmes. It is terror.' She raised her veil as she spoke, and we could see that she was indeed in a pitiable state of agitation, her face all drawn and grey, with restless, frightened eyes, like those of some hunted animal. Her features and figure were those of a woman of thirty, but her hair was shot with premature grey, and her expression was weary and haggard. Sherlock Holmes ran her over with one of his quick, all-comprehensive glances.

'You must not fear,' said he, soothingly, bending forward and patting her forearm. 'We shall soon set matters right, I have no doubt. You have come in by train this morning, I see.'

'You know me, then?'

'No, but I observe the second half of a return ticket in the palm of your left glove. You must have started early and yet you had a good drive in a dog-cart, along heavy roads, before you reached the station.'

The lady gave a violent start, and stared in bewilderment at my companion.

'There is no mystery, my dear madam,' said he, smiling. 'The left arm of your jacket is spattered with mud in no less than seven places. The marks are perfectly fresh. There is no vehicle save a dog-cart which throws up mud in that way, and then only when you sit on the left-hand side of the driver.'

'Whatever your reasons may be, you are perfectly correct,' said she. 'I started from home before six, reached Leatherhead at twenty past, and came in by the first train to Waterloo. Sir, I can stand this strain no longer, I shall go mad if it continues. I have no one to turn to – none, save only one, who cares for me, and he, poor fellow, can be of little aid. I have heard of you, Mr Holmes; I have heard of you from Mrs Farintosh, whom you helped in the hour of her sore need. It was from her that I had your address. Oh, sir, do you not think you could help me too, and at least throw a little light through the dense darkness which surrounds me? At present it is out of my power to reward you for your services, but in a month or two I shall be married, with the control of my own income, and then at least you shall not find me ungrateful.'

Holmes turned to his desk, and unlocking it, drew out a small case-book which he consulted.

COMMENTARY

The woman appears distressed. Holmes surprises her by being able to tell her a lot about herself and the way in which she has travelled up to London. The woman says that, although she does not have much money, she would like to ask Holmes's advice.

pitiable: pitiful
premature: before its time
all-comprehensive glances: a look which took in everything
dog-cart: an open horse-drawn cart
save: except for
sore: desperate

'Farintosh,' said he. 'Ah, yes, I recall the case; it was concerned with an opal tiara. I think it was before your time, Watson. I can only say, madam, that I shall be happy to devote the same care to your case as I did to that of your friend. As to reward, my profession is its reward; but you are at liberty to defray whatever expenses I may be put to, at the time which suits you best. And now I beg that you will lay before us everything that may help us in forming an opinion upon the matter.'

'Alas!' replied our visitor. 'The very horror of my situation lies in the fact that my fears are so vague, and my suspicions depend so entirely upon small points, which might seem trivial to another, that even he to whom of all others I have a right to look for help and advice looks upon all that I tell him about it as the fancies of a nervous woman. He does not say so, but I can read it from his soothing answers and averted eyes. But I have heard, Mr Holmes, that you can see deeply into the manifold wickedness of the human heart. You may advise me how to walk amid the dangers which encompass me.'

'I am all attention, madam.'

'My name is Helen Stoner, and I am living with my step-father, who is the last survivor of one of the oldest Saxon families in England; the Roylotts of Stoke Moran, on the western border of Surrey.'

Holmes nodded his head. 'The name is familiar to me,' said he.

'The family was at one time among the richest in England, and the estate extended over the borders into Berkshire in the north, and Hampshire in the west. In the last century, however, four successive heirs were of a dissolute and wasteful disposition, and the family ruin was eventually completed by a gambler, in the days of the Regency. Nothing was left save a few acres of ground, and the two-hundred-year-old house, which is itself crushed under a heavy mortgage. The last squire dragged out his existence there, living the horrible life of an aristocratic pauper; but his only son, my stepfather, seeing that he must adapt himself to the new conditions, obtained an advance from a relative, which enabled him to take a medical degree, and went out to Calcutta, where, by his professional skill and his force of character, he

---

tiara: small jewelled headband
defray: pay for
averted: turned away
manifold: varied
encompass: surround
dissolute: immoral
mortgage: money borrowed against the value of the house

COMMENTARY
A friend has recommended Holmes as somebody who can help her. She is afraid that what she has to say will sound as if it has little to do with crime. The woman says her name is Helen Stoner, and that she lives with her stepfather.

established a large practice. In a fit of anger, however, caused by some robberies which had been perpetrated in the house, he beat his native butler to death, and narrowly escaped a capital sentence. As it was, he suffered a long term of imprisonment, and afterwards returned to England a morose and *[sad]* disappointed man.

'When Dr Roylott was in India he married my mother, Mrs Stoner, the young widow of Major-General Stoner, of the Bengal Artillery. My sister Julia and I were twins, and we were only two years old at the time of my mother's re-marriage. She had a considerable sum of money, not less than a thousand a year, and this she bequeathed to Dr Roylott entirely whilst we resided with him, with a provision that a certain annual sum should be allowed to each of us in the event of our marriage. Shortly after our return to England my mother died—she was killed eight years ago in a railway accident near Crewe. Dr Roylott then abandoned his attempts to establish himself in practice in London, and took us to live with him in the ancestral house at Stoke Moran. *[family]* The money which my mother had left was enough for all our wants, and there seemed no obstacle to our happiness.

'But a terrible change came over our stepfather about this time. Instead of making friends and exchanging visits with our neighbours, who had at first been overjoyed to see a Roylott of Stoke Moran back in the old family seat, he shut himself up in his house, and seldom came out save to indulge in ferocious quarrels with whoever might cross his path. Violence of temper approaching to *[runs in the family]* mania has been hereditary in the men of the family, and in my stepfather's case it had, I believe, been intensified by his long residence in the tropics. A series of disgraceful brawls took place, two of which ended in the police-court, until at last he became the terror of the village, and the folks would fly at his approach, for he is a man of immense strength, and absolutely uncontrollable in his anger.

'Last week he hurled the local blacksmith over a parapet into a stream and it was only by paying over all the money that I could gather together that I was able to avert another public exposure. He had no friends at all save the

COMMENTARY

Dr Roylott married Helen's mother when they were all living in India. Soon after the marriage, Helen's family returned to England. Dr Roylott had always been difficult to live with, but he became increasingly strange and ill-tempered, particularly after the death of his wife.

perpetrated: carried out
capital: death
morose: silent, bad-tempered
entirely: alone
ancestral: family
mania: madness
fly: run away

gypsys

wandering gipsies, and he would give these vagabonds leave to encamp upon the few acres of bramble-covered land which represent the family éstate, and would accept in return the hospitality of their tents, wandering away with them sometimes for weeks on end. He has a passion also for Indian animals, which are sent over to him by a correspondent, and he has at this moment a cheetah and a baboon, which wander freely over his grounds, and are feared by the villagers almost as much as their master.

'You can imagine from what I say that my poor sister Julia and I had no great pleasure in our lives. No servant would stay with us, and for a long time we did all the work of the house. She was but thirty at the time of her death, and yet her hair had already begun to whiten, even as mine has.'

'Your sister is dead, then?'

been maybe murder

'She died just two years ago, and it is of her death that I wish to speak to you. You can understand that, living the life which I have described, we were little likely to see anyone of our own age and position. We had, however, an aunt, my mother's maiden sister, Miss Honoria Westphail, who lives near Harrow, and we were occasionally allowed to pay short visits at this lady's house. Julia went there at Christmas two years ago, and met there a half-pay Major of Marines, to whom she became engaged. My stepfather learned of the engagement when my sister returned, and offered no objection to the marriage; but within a fortnight of the day which had been fixed for the wedding, the terrible event occurred which has deprived me of my only companion.'

un married

Sherlock Holmes had been leaning back in his chair with his eyes closed, and his head sunk in a cushion, but he half opened his lids now, and glanced across at his visitor.

'Pray be precise as to details,' said he.

burnt

'It is easy for me to be so, for every event of that dreadful time is seared into my memory. The manor house is, as I have already said, very old, and only one wing is now inhabited. The bedrooms in this wing are on the ground floor, the sitting-rooms being in the central block of the buildings. Of these

do not use

an of house

vagabonds: wandering people

correspondent: somebody with whom you exchange letters

maiden: unmarried

half-pay Major of Marines: a major in the Royal Marines (soldiers who served on board ship), who had retired on half his salary

seared: burnt

COMMENTARY

Helen's stepfather kept exotic pets sent to him from India, and behaved in ever more wild and violent ways. Helen tells Holmes how, although they lived a quiet and sheltered life, her sister met a young man and became engaged to be married. Two weeks before her marriage, however, she died very suddenly. Holmes asks her to go into detail, and she begins by describing the layout of the house.

bedrooms the first is Dr Roylott's, the second my sister's, and the third my own. There is no communication between them, but they all open out into the same corridor. Do I make myself plain?'

'Perfectly so.'

'The windows of the three rooms open out upon the lawn. That fatal night Dr Roylott had gone to his room early, though we knew that he had not retired to rest, for my sister was troubled by the smell of the strong Indian cigars which it was his custom to smoke. She left her room, therefore, and came into mine, where she sat for some time, chatting about her approaching wedding. At eleven o'clock she rose to leave me, but she paused at the door and looked back.

'"Tell me, Helen," said she, "have you ever heard anyone whistle in the dead of the night?"

'"Never," said I.

'"I suppose that you could not possibly whistle yourself in your sleep?"

'"Certainly not. But why?"

'"Because during the last few nights I have always, about three in the morning, heard a low clear whistle. I am a light sleeper, and it has awakened me. I cannot tell where it came from – perhaps from the next room, perhaps from the lawn. I thought that I would just ask you whether you had heard it."

'"No, I have not. It must be those wretched gipsies in the plantation."

'"Very likely. And yet if it were on the lawn I wonder that you did not hear it also."

'"Ah, but I sleep more heavily than you."

'"Well, it is of no great consequence, at any rate," she smiled back at me, closed my door, and a few moments later I heard her key turn in the lock.'

'Indeed,' said Holmes. 'Was it your custom always to lock yourselves in at night?'

'Always.'

'And why?'

COMMENTARY

Helen relates the last conversation she ever had with her sister, when she was asked if she had ever heard a whistle in the night. Helen said she had not. Then the two young women separated, each to go to their own rooms. They locked themselves in because of the strange and dangerous pets which roamed the grounds.

communication: door from one into the other

consequence: importance

'I think that I mentioned to you that the Doctor kept a cheetah and a baboon. We had no feeling of security unless our doors were locked.'

'Quite so. Pray proceed with your statement.'

'I could not sleep that night. A vague feeling of impending misfortune impressed me. My sister and I, you will recollect, were twins, and you know how subtle are the links which bind two souls which are so closely allied. It was a wild night. The wind was howling outside, and the rain was beating and splashing against the windows. Suddenly, amidst all the hubbub of the gale, there burst forth the wild scream of a terrified woman. I knew that it was my sister's voice. I sprang from my bed, wrapped a shawl round me, and rushed into the corridor. As I opened my door I seemed to hear a low whistle, such as my sister described, and a few moments later a clanging sound, as if a mass of metal had fallen. As I ran down the passage my sister's door was unlocked, and revolved slowly upon its hinges. I stared at it horror-stricken, not knowing what was about to issue from it. By the light of the corridor lamp I saw my sister appear at the opening, her face blanched with terror, her hands groping for help, her whole figure swaying to and fro like that of a drunkard. I ran to her and threw my arms round her, but at that moment her knees seemed to give way and she fell to the ground. She writhed as one who is in terrible pain, and her limbs were dreadfully convulsed. At first I thought that she had not recognised me, but as I bent over her she suddenly shrieked out in a voice which I shall never forget, "Oh, my God! Helen! It was the band! The speckled band!" There was something else which she would fain have said, and she stabbed with her finger into the air in the direction of the Doctor's room, but a fresh convulsion seized her and choked her words. I rushed out, calling loudly for my stepfather, and I met him hastening from his room in his dressing-gown. When he reached my sister's side she was unconscious, and though he poured brandy down her throat, and sent for medical aid from the village, all efforts were in vain, for she slowly sank and died without having recovered her consciousness. Such was the dreadful end of my beloved sister.'

We had no feeling of security: we did not
   feel safe
impending misfortune: something dreadful
   about to happen
hubbub: noise
blanched: white
convulsed: stiff and shaking
would fain have said: wanted to say

COMMENTARY
During the night, Helen heard her sister cry out. Unlocking her own door, she hurried out to find her sister in the corridor, thrashing about, and saying something about a 'speckled band'. She was still trying to say more when she died.

'One moment,' said Holmes: 'are you sure about this whistle and metallic sound? Could you swear to it?'

'That was what the county coroner asked me at the inquiry. It is my strong impression that I heard it, and yet among the crash of the gale, and the creaking of an old house, I may possibly have been deceived.'

'Was your sister dressed?'

'No, she was in her nightdress. In her right hand was found the charred stump of a match, and in her left a matchbox.'

'Showing that she had struck a light and looked about her when the alarm took place. That is important. And what conclusions did the coroner come to?'

'He investigated the case with great care, for Dr Roylott's conduct had long been notorious in the county, but he was unable to find any satisfactory cause of death. My evidence showed that the door had been fastened upon the inner side, and the windows were blocked by old-fashioned shutters with broad iron bars, which were secured every night. The walls were carefully sounded, and were shown to be quite solid all round, and the flooring was also thoroughly examined, with the same result. The chimney is wide, but is barred up by four large staples. It is certain, therefore, that my sister was quite alone when she met her end. Besides, there were no marks of any violence upon her.'

'How about poison?'

'The doctors examined her for it, but without success.'

'What do you think that this unfortunate lady died of, then?'

'It is my belief that she died of pure fear and nervous shock, though what it was which frightened her I cannot imagine.'

'Were there gipsies in the plantation at the time?'

'Yes, there are nearly always some there.'

'Ah, and what did you gather from this allusion to a band – a speckled band?'

'Sometimes I have thought that it was merely the wild talk of delirium, sometimes that it may have referred to some band of people, perhaps to these very gipsies in the plantation. I do not know whether

COMMENTARY

Although there was an inquest to investigate the young woman's sudden death, no evidence of foul play could be found. The shutters to her bedroom had not been tampered with. Holmes asks Helen what *she* thinks happened. She suggests that the gipsies who stay in the grounds might have had some part in her sister's death.

county coroner: a court official whose job is to find out the cause of any sudden death in the county

notorious: well-known, usually for bad reasons

sounded: examined by tapping

staples: metal posts

allusion: reference

delirium: high fever

the spotted handkerchiefs which so many of them wear over their heads might have suggested the strange adjective which she used.'

Holmes shook his head like a man who is far from being satisfied.

'These are very deep waters,' said he; 'pray go on with your narrative.'

'Two years have passed since then, and my life has been until lately lonelier than ever. A month ago, however, a dear friend, whom I have known for many years, has done me the honour to ask my hand in marriage. His name is Armitage – Percy Armitage – the second son of Mr Armitage, of Crane Water, near Reading. My stepfather has offered no opposition to the match, and we are to be married in the course of the spring. Two days ago some repairs were started in the west wing of the building, and my bedroom wall has been pierced, so that I have had to move into the chamber in which my sister died, and to sleep in the very bed in which she slept. Imagine, then, my thrill of terror when last night, as I lay awake, thinking over her terrible fate, I suddenly heard in the silence of the night the low whistle which had been the herald of her own death. I sprang up and lit the lamp, but nothing was to be seen in the room. I was too shaken to go to bed again, however, so I dressed, and as soon as it was daylight I slipped down, got a dog-cart at the Crown Inn, which is opposite, and drove to Leatherhead, from whence I have come on this morning, with the one object of seeing you and asking your advice.'

'You have done wisely,' said my friend. 'But have you told me all?'

'Yes, all.'

'Miss Stoner, you have not. You are screening your stepfather.'

'Why, what do you mean?'

For answer Holmes pushed back the frill of black lace which fringed the hand that lay upon our visitor's knee. Five little livid spots, the marks of four fingers and a thumb, were printed upon the white wrist.

'You have been cruelly used,' said Holmes.

The lady coloured deeply, and covered over her injured wrist. 'He is a hard man,' she said, 'and perhaps he hardly knows his own strength.'

---

the spotted handkerchiefs…heads: many gipsies at the time, both men and women, wore brightly coloured cotton headscarves

thrill: shudder

herald: signal

screening: protecting

livid: black and blue

COMMENTARY

Helen herself is now engaged to be married. Her stepfather has started some rebuilding on the house which means that she now sleeps in her sister's room. She too has heard a whistle in the night. Helen tells Holmes that she is so frightened that she slipped out of the house to ask his advice. He tells her she was quite right to do so.

There was a long silence, during which Holmes leaned his chin upon his hands and stared into the crackling fire.

'This is very deep business,' he said at last. 'There are a thousand details which I should desire to know before I decide upon our course of action. Yet we have not a moment to lose. If we were to come to Stoke Moran to-day, would it be possible for us to see over these rooms without the knowledge of your stepfather?'

'As it happens, he spoke of coming into town to-day upon some most important business. It is probable that he will be away all day, and that there would be nothing to disturb you. We have a housekeeper now, but she is old and foolish, and I could easily get her out of the way.'

'Excellent. You are not averse to this trip, Watson?'

'By no means.'

'Then we shall both come. What are you going to do yourself?'

'I have one or two things which I would wish to do now that I am in town. But I shall return by the twelve o'clock train, so as to be there in time for your coming.'

'And you may expect us early in the afternoon. I have myself some small business matters to attend to. Will you not wait and breakfast?'

'No, I must go. My heart is lightened already since I have confided my trouble to you. I shall look forward to seeing you again this afternoon.' She dropped her thick black veil over her face, and glided from the room.

'And what do you think of it all, Watson?' asked Sherlock Holmes, leaning back in his chair.

'It seems to me to be a most dark and sinister business.'

'Dark enough, and sinister enough.'

'Yet if the lady is correct in saying that the flooring and walls are sound, and that the door, window, and chimney are impassable, then her sister must have been undoubtedly alone when she met her mysterious end.'

'What becomes, then, of these nocturnal whistles, and what of the very peculiar words of the dying woman?'

'I cannot think.'

COMMENTARY

Holmes decides that he and Watson will travel down to the house that afternoon, avoiding Dr Roylott, who is in London on business. Helen leaves, agreeing to meet the two men later. Holmes mulls over possible solutions to the mystery.

into town: to London
averse: opposed
sinister: wicked
nocturnal: night-time

1st opinion (Sherlock holmes)

'When you combine the ideas of whistles at night, the presence of a band of gipsies who are on intimate terms with this old doctor, the fact that we have every reason to believe that the doctor has an interest in preventing his stepdaughter's marriage, the dying allusion to a band, and finally, the fact that Miss Helen Stoner heard a metallic clang, which might have been caused by one of those metal bars which secured the shutters falling back into their place, I think there is good ground to think that the mystery may be cleared along these lines.'

'But what, then, did the gipsies do?'

'I cannot imagine.'

'I see many objections to any such a theory.'

'And so do I. It is precisely for that reason that we are going to Stoke Moran this day. I want to see whether the objections are fatal, or if they may be explained away. But what, in the name of the devil!'

The ejaculation had been drawn from my companion by the fact that our door had been suddenly dashed open, and that a huge man framed himself in the aperture. His costume was a peculiar mixture of the professional and of the agricultural, having a black top-hat, a long frock-coat, and a pair of high gaiters, with a hunting-crop swinging in his hand. So tall was he that his hat actually brushed the cross bar of the doorway, and his breadth seemed to span it across from side to side. A large face, seared with a thousand wrinkles, burned yellow with the sun, and marked with every evil passion, was turned from one to the other of us, while his deep-set, bile-shot eyes, and the high thin fleshless nose, gave him somewhat the resemblance to a fierce old bird of prey.

'Which of you is Holmes?' asked this apparition.

'My name, sir, but you have the advantage of me,' said my companion, quietly.

'I am Dr Grimesby Roylott, of Stoke Moran.'

'Indeed, Doctor,' said Holmes, blandly. 'Pray take a seat.'

'I will do nothing of the kind. My stepdaughter has been here. I have traced her. What has she been saying to you?'

'It is a little cold for the time of the year,' said Holmes.

intimate: friendly
ejaculation: sudden remark
aperture: doorway
gaiters: coverings of cloth or leather worn on the lower leg
hunting-crop: whip
bile-shot: yellow, unhealthy

COMMENTARY
Watson and Holmes are sitting quietly discussing the case when Dr Roylott bursts into the room. He demands to know what his stepdaughter has been saying to you. Holmes refuses to answer.

'What has she been saying to you?' screamed the old man furiously.

'But I have heard that the crocuses promise well,' continued my companion imperturbably.

'Ha! You put me off, do you?' said our new visitor, taking a step forward, and shaking his hunting-crop. 'I know you, you scoundrel! I have heard of you before. You are Holmes the meddler.'

My friend smiled.

'Holmes the busybody!!'

His smile broadened.

'Holmes the Scotland Yard jack-in-office.'

Holmes chuckled heartily. 'Your conversation is most entertaining,' said he. 'When you go out close the door, for there is a decided draught.'

'I will go when I have had my say. Don't you dare to meddle with my affairs. I know that Miss Stoner has been here – I traced her! I am a dangerous man to fall foul of! See here.' He stepped swiftly forward, seized the poker, and bent it into a curve with his huge brown hands.

'See that you keep yourself out of my grip,' he snarled, and hurling the twisted poker into the fireplace, he strode out of the room.

'He seems a very amiable person,' said Holmes, laughing. 'I am not quite so bulky, but, if he had remained I might have shown him that my grip was not much more feeble than his own.' As he spoke he picked up the steel poker, and with a sudden effort straightened it out again.

'Fancy his having the insolence to confound me with the official detective force! This incident gives zest to our investigation, however, and I only trust that our little friend will not suffer from her imprudence in allowing this brute to trace her. And now, Watson, we shall order breakfast, and afterwards I shall walk down to Doctors' Commons, where I hope to get some data which may help us in this matter.'

It was nearly one o'clock when Sherlock Holmes returned from his excursion. He held in his hand a sheet of blue paper, scrawled over with notes and figures.

COMMENTARY

Dr Roylott leaves in a fury, having insulted and threatened Holmes, and demonstrated his strength by bending the poker. Holmes quietly straightens the poker and sets off to make some investigations into Dr Roylott's financial position.

imperturbably: calmly

meddler: one who interferes

Scotland Yard jack-in-office: a servant of the official police

amiable: charming, pleasant

confound: confuse

Doctors' Commons: the headquarters of the Doctors of Civil Law, where all sorts of legal papers were stored

data: facts, information

'I have seen the will of the deceased wife,' said he. 'To determine its exact meaning I have been obliged to work out the present prices of the investments with which it is concerned. The total income, which at the time of the wife's death was little short of £1,100, is now through the fall in agricultural prices not more than £750. Each daughter can claim an income of £250, in case of marriage. It is evident therefore, that if both girls had married, this beauty would have had a mere pittance, while even one of them would cripple him to a serious extent. My morning's work has not been wasted, since it has proved that he has the very strongest motives for standing in the way of anything of the sort. And now, Watson, this is too serious for dawdling, especially as the old man is aware that we are interesting ourselves in his affairs, so if you are ready we shall call a cab and drive to Waterloo. I should be very much obliged if you would slip your revolver into your pocket. An Eley's No. 2 is an Hand gun excellent argument with gentlemen who can twist steel pokers into knots. That and a tooth-brush are, I think, all that we need.'

PAUSE FOR PLAYBACK:
Now look at the playback questions on page 66 before going on with your reading.

▮▮

Look out for...
- **the way in which Holmes examines the house. How do his findings fit in with the theories he has already formed?**
- **the way in which Holmes has Helen Stoner move rooms. What are his reasons?**
- **the meaning of the 'speckled band'. Does it fit in with the ideas that you have had?**

At Waterloo we were fortunate in catching a train for Leatherhead, where we hired a trap at the station inn, and drove for four or five miles through the

this beauty: that is, Doctor Roylott
pittance: very small amount of money
dawdling: going slowly
Eley's No. 2: a kind of hand gun
trap: horse-drawn carriage

COMMENTARY
Holmes returns at the end of the morning, having found out that, by the terms of his dead wife's will, Dr Roylott will be ruined if either of his stepdaughters marry. Holmes and Watson set off for the house, taking the care to arm themselves, as the case is becoming dangerous.

lovely Surrey lanes. It was a perfect day, with a bright sun and a few fleecy clouds in the heavens. The trees and wayside hedges were just throwing out their first green shoots, and the air was full of the pleasant smell of the moist earth. To me at least there was a strange contrast between the sweet promise of the spring and this sinister quest upon which we were engaged. My companion sat in front of the trap, his arms folded, his hat pulled down over his eyes, and his chin sunk upon his breast, buried in the deepest thought. Suddenly, however, he started, tapped me on the shoulder, and pointed over the meadows.

'Look there!' said he.

A heavily-timbered park stretched up in a gentle slope, thickening into a grove at the highest point. From amidst the branches there jutted out the grey gables and high roof-tree of a very old mansion.

'Stoke Moran?' said he.

'Yes, sir, that be the house of Dr Grimesby Roylott,' remarked the driver.

'There is some building going on there,' said Holmes: 'that is where we are going.'

'There's the village,' said the driver, pointing to a cluster of roofs some distance to the left; 'but if you want to get to the house, you'll find it shorter to go over this stile, and so by the footpath over the fields. There it is, where the lady is walking.'

'And the lady, I fancy, is Miss Stoner,' observed Holmes, shading his eyes. 'Yes, I think we had better do as you suggest.'

We got off, paid our fare, and the trap rattled back on its way to Leatherhead.

'I thought it as well,' said Holmes, as we climbed the stile, 'that this fellow should think we had come here as architects, or on some definite business. It may stop his gossip. Good afternoon, Miss Stoner. You see that we have been as good as our word.'

Our client of the morning had hurried forward to meet us with a face which spoke her joy. 'I have been waiting so eagerly for you,' she cried, shaking hands

grove: wood

COMMENTARY
Holmes and Watson arrive at Stoke Moran and are met by Helen, who tells them that Dr Roylott is away for the day.

with us warmly. 'All has turned out splendidly. Dr Roylott has gone to town, and it is unlikely that he will be back before evening.'

'We have had the pleasure of making the Doctor's acquaintance,' said Holmes, and in a few words he sketched out what had occurred. Miss Stoner turned white to the lips as she listened.

'Good heavens!' she cried, 'he has followed me, then.'

'So it appears.'

'He is so cunning that I never know when I am safe from him. What will he say when he returns?'

'He must guard himself, for he may find that there is someone more cunning than himself upon his track. You must lock yourself from him to-night. If he is violent, we shall take you away to your aunt's at Harrow. Now, we must make the best use of our time, so kindly take us at once to the rooms which we are to examine.'

The building was of grey, lichen-blotched stone, with a high central portion, and two curving wings, like the claws of a crab, thrown out on each side. In one of these wings the windows were broken, and blocked with wooden boards, while the roof was partly caved in, a picture of ruin. The central portion was in little better repair, but the right-hand block was comparatively modern, and the blinds in the windows, with the blue smoke curling up from the chimneys, showed that this was where the family resided. Some scaffolding had been erected against the end wall, and the stone-work had been broken into, but there were no signs of any workmen at the moment of our visit. Holmes walked slowly up and down the ill-trimmed lawn, and examined with deep attention the outsides of the windows.

'This, I take it, belongs to the room in which you used to sleep, the centre one to your sister's, and the one next to the main building to Dr Roylott's chamber?'

'Exactly so. But I am now sleeping in the middle one.'

'Pending the alterations, as I understand. By the way, there does not seem to be any very pressing need for repairs at that end wall.'

---

lichen-blotched: covered in patches of
   greeny-grey moss
ill-trimmed: untidily cut
pending: during

'There were none. I believe that it was an excuse to move me from my room.'

'Ah! that is suggestive. Now, on the other side of this narrow wing runs the corridor from which these three rooms open. There are windows in it, of course?'

'Yes, but very small ones. Too narrow for anyone to pass through.'

'As you both locked your doors at night, your rooms were unapproachable from that side. Now, would you have the kindness to go into your room, and to bar your shutters.'

Miss Stoner did so, and Holmes, after a careful examination through the open window, endeavoured in every way to force the shutter open, but without success. There was no slit through which a knife could be passed to raise the bar. Then with his lens he tested the hinges, but they were of solid iron, built firmly into the massive masonry. 'Hum!' said he, scratching his chin in some perplexity, 'my theory certainly presents some difficulties. No one could pass these shutters if they were bolted. Well, we shall see if the inside throws any light upon the matter.'

A small side-door led into the whitewashed corridor from which the three bedrooms opened. Holmes refused to examine the third chamber, so we passed at once to the second, that in which Miss Stoner was now sleeping, and in which her sister had met her fate. It was a homely little room, with a low ceiling and a gaping fireplace, after the fashion of old country houses. A brown chest of drawers stood in one corner, a narrow white-counterpaned bed in another, and a dressing-table on the left-hand side of the window. These articles, with two small wickerwork chairs, made up all the furniture in the room, save for a square of Wilton carpet in the centre. The boards round and the panelling of the walls were brown, worm-eaten oak, so old and discoloured that it may have dated from the original building of the house. Holmes drew one of the chairs into a corner and sat silent, while his eyes travelled round and round and up and down, taking in every detail of the apartment.

'Where does that bell communicate with?' he asked at last, pointing to a thick bell-rope which hung down beside the bed, the tassel actually lying upon the pillow.

is suggestive: gives an important clue

Wilton: a particular kind of carpet made in Wilton, in Wiltshire

panelling: wood covering on the walls

bell-rope: it was usual in large houses to have a system of wires attached to bells in the kitchen, or the servants' quarters, so that the owners could call a servant simply by tugging on the bell-rope

'It goes to the housekeeper's room.'

'It looks newer than the other things?'

'Yes, it was only put there a couple of years ago.'

'Your sister asked for it, I suppose?'

'No, I never heard of her using it. We used always to get what we wanted for ourselves.'

'Indeed, it seemed unnecessary to put so nice a bell-pull there. You will excuse me for a few minutes while I satisfy myself as to this floor.' He threw himself down upon his face with his lens in his hand, and crawled swiftly backwards and forwards, examining minutely the cracks between the boards. Then he did the same with the woodwork with which the chamber was panelled. Finally he walked over to the bed and spent some time in staring at it, and in running his eye up and down the wall. Finally he took the bell-rope in his hand and gave it a brisk tug.

'Why, it's a dummy,' said he.

'Won't it ring?'

'No, it is not even attached to a wire. This is very interesting. You can see now that it is fastened to a hook just above where the little opening of the ventilator is.'

'How very absurd! I never noticed that before.'

'Very strange!' muttered Holmes, pulling at the rope. 'There are one or two very singular points about this room. For example, what a fool a builder must be to open a ventilator into another room, when, with the same trouble, he might have communicated with the outside air!'

'That is also quite modern,' said the lady.

'Done about the same time as the bell-rope?' remarked Holmes.

'Yes, there were several little changes carried out about that time.'

'They seem to have been of a most interesting character – dummy bell-ropes, and ventilators which do not ventilate. With your permission, Miss Stoner, we shall now carry our researches into the inner apartment.'

Dr Grimesby Roylott's chamber was larger than that of his stepdaughter,

---

dummy: false, not in working order

ventilator: a special opening in a wall which allowed stale air out and fresh air in

singular: strange, unusual

chamber: bedroom

COMMENTARY

Holmes examines the floor and the wooden panelling. He discovers that the bell-rope in the bedroom does not work, and that the ventilator, instead of leading to the air outside, gives onto another room. He finds out that both ventilator and bell-rope were put in at the same time.

but was as plainly furnished. A camp bed, a small wooden shelf full of books, mostly of a technical character, an armchair beside the bed, a plain wooden chair against the wall, a round table, and a large iron safe were the principal things which met the eye. Holmes walked slowly round and examined each and all of them with the keenest interest.

'What's in here?' he asked, tapping the safe.

'My stepfather's business papers.'

'Oh! you have seen inside then?'

'Only once, some years ago. I remember that it was full of papers.'

'There isn't a cat in it, for example?'

'No. What a strange idea!'

'Well, look at this!' He took up a small saucer of milk which stood on the top of it.

'No; we don't keep a cat. But there is a cheetah and a baboon.'

'Ah, yes, of course! Well, a cheetah is just a big cat, and yet a saucer of milk does not go very far in satisfying its wants, I daresay. There is one point which I should wish to determine.' He squatted down in front of the wooden chair, and examined the seat of it with the greatest attention.

'Thank you. That is quite settled,' said he, rising and putting his lens in his pocket. 'Hello! here is something interesting!'

The object which had caught his eye was a small dog lash hung on one corner of the bed. The lash, however, was curled upon itself, and tied so as to make a loop of whipcord.

'What do you make of that, Watson?'

'It's a common enough lash. But I don't know why it should be tied.'

'That is not quite so common, is it? Ah, me! it's a wicked world, and when a clever man turns his brain to crime it is the worst of all. I think that I have seen enough now, Miss Stoner, and, with your permission, we shall walk out upon the lawn.'

I had never seen my friend's face so grim, or his brow so dark, as it was when we turned from the scene of his investigation. We had walked several

COMMENTARY

The next room is Dr Roylott's bedroom, which Holmes examines carefully. He notices that a saucer of milk has been placed on top of the Doctor's iron safe. Holmes leaves the room feeling extremely troubled.

technical character: scientific kind
determine: be sure of
lash: whip

times up and down the lawn, neither Miss Stoner nor myself liking to break in upon his thoughts before he roused himself from his reverie.

'It is very essential, Miss Stoner,' said he, 'that you should absolutely follow my advice in every respect.'

'I shall most certainly do so.'

'The matter is too serious for any hesitation. Your life may depend upon your compliance.'

'I assure you that I am in your hands.'

'In the first place, both my friend and I must spend the night in your room.'

Both Miss Stoner and I gazed at him in astonishment.

'Yes, it must be so. Let me explain. I believe that that is the village inn over there?'

'Yes, that is the "Crown".'

'Very good. Your windows would be visible from there?'

'Certainly.'

'You must confine yourself to your room, on pretence of a headache, when your stepfather comes back. Then when you hear him retire for the night, you must open the shutters of your window, undo the hasp, put your lamp there as a signal to us, and then withdraw with everything which you are likely to want into the room which you used to occupy. I have no doubt that, in spite of the repairs, you could manage there for one night.'

'Oh, yes, easily.'

'The rest you will leave in our hands.'

'But what will you do?'

'We shall spend the night in your room, and we shall investigate the cause of this noise which has disturbed you.'

'I believe, Mr Holmes, that you have already made up your mind,' said Miss Stoner, laying her hand upon my companion's sleeve.

'Perhaps I have.'

'Then for pity's sake tell me what was the cause of my sister's death.'

'I should prefer to have clearer proof before I speak.'

reverie: private thoughts
compliance: agreement
confine: keep

COMMENTARY

Holmes tells Helen it is important that he and Watson spend the night in her bedroom without Dr Roylott knowing. They will wait in the village inn for her to signal that her stepfather has gone to bed. Once she has signalled, Helen must go and sleep in her old room. Holmes and Watson will wait in her bedroom for further developments.

'You can at least tell me whether my own thought is correct, and if she died from some sudden fright.'

'No, I do not think so. I think that there was probably some more tangible cause. And now, Miss Stoner, we must leave you, for if Dr Roylott returned and saw us, our journey would be in vain. Good-bye, and be brave, for if you will do what I have told you, you may rest assured that we shall soon drive away the dangers that threaten you.'

Sherlock Holmes and I had no difficulty in engaging a bedroom and sitting-room at the Crown Inn. They were on the upper floor, and from our window we could command a view of the avenue gate, and of the inhabited wing of Stoke Moran Manor House. At dusk we saw Dr Grimesby Roylott drive past, his huge form looming up beside the little figure of the lad who drove him. The boy had some slight difficulty in undoing the heavy iron gates, and we heard the hoarse roar of the Doctor's voice, and saw the fury with which he shook his clenched fists at him. The trap drove on, and a few minutes later we saw a sudden light spring up among the trees as the lamp was lit in one of the sitting-rooms.

'Do you know, Watson,' said Holmes, as we sat together in the gathering darkness, 'I have really some scruples as to taking you tonight. There is a distinct element of danger.'

'Can I be of assistance?'

'Your presence might be invaluable.'

'Then I shall certainly come.'

'It is very kind of you.'

'You speak of danger. You have evidently seen more in these rooms than was visible to me.'

'No, but I fancy that I may have deduced a little more. I imagine that you saw all that I did.'

'I saw nothing remarkable save the bell-rope, and what purpose that could answer I confess is more than I can imagine.'

'You saw the ventilator, too?'

COMMENTARY

Holmes and Watson make their way to the local inn to wait for Helen's signal. As they wait, they see Dr Roylott return as darkness falls. They discuss the case. Holmes is concerned that there is great danger lying in wait for all of them.

tangible: real, external
engaging: hiring
scruples: worries, reservations

'Yes, but I do not think that it is such a very unusual thing to have a small opening between two rooms. It was so small that a rat could hardly pass through.'

'I knew that we should find a ventilator before ever we came to Stoke Moran.'

'My dear Holmes!'

'Oh, yes, I did. You remember in her statement she said that her sister could smell Dr Roylott's cigar. Now, of course that suggests at once that there must be a communication between the two rooms. It could only be a small one, or it would have been remarked upon at the Coroner's inquiry. I deduced a ventilator.'

'But what harm can there be in that?'

'Well, there is at least a curious coincidence of dates. A ventilator is made, a cord is hung, and a lady who sleeps in the bed dies. Does not that strike you?'

'I cannot as yet see any connection.'

'Did you observe anything very peculiar about that bed?'

'No.'

'It was clamped to the floor. Did you ever see a bed fastened like that before?'

'I cannot say that I have.'

'The lady could not move her bed. It must always be in the same relative position to the ventilator and to the rope – for so we may call it, since it was clearly never meant for a bell-pull.'

'Holmes,' I cried, 'I seem to see dimly what you are hitting at. We are only just in time to prevent some subtle and horrible crime.'

'Subtle enough, and horrible enough. When a doctor does go wrong, he is the first of criminals. He has nerve and he has knowledge. Palmer and Pritchard were among the heads of their profession. This man strikes even deeper, but, I think, Watson, that we shall be able to strike deeper still. But we shall have horrors enough before the night is over: for goodness' sake let us have a quiet pipe, and turn our minds for a few hours to something more cheerful.'

---

remarked upon: pointed out
Palmer and Pritchard: well-known criminals
  of the time

COMMENTARY
Holmes talks about what he has found out by examining the rooms. He had expected to find the ventilator between Dr Roylott's room and Helen's sister's.

About nine o'clock the light among the trees was extinguished, and all was dark in the direction of the Manor House. Two hours passed slowly away, and then, suddenly, just at the stroke of eleven, a single bright light shone out right in front of us.

'That is our signal,' said Holmes, springing to his feet; 'it comes from the middle window.'

As we passed out he exchanged a few words with the landlord, explaining that we were going on a late visit to an acquaintance, and that it was possible that we might spend the night there. A moment later we were out on the dark road, a chill wind blowing in our faces, and one yellow light twinkling in front of us through the gloom to guide us on our sombre errand.

There was little difficulty in entering the grounds, for unrepaired breaches gaped in the old park wall. Making our way among the trees, we reached the lawn, crossed it, and were about to enter through the window, when out from a clump of laurel bushes there darted what seemed to be a hideous and distorted child, who threw itself on the grass with writhing limbs, and then ran swiftly across the lawn into the darkness.

'My God!' I whispered, 'did you see it?'

Holmes was for the moment as startled as I. His hand closed like a vice upon my wrist in his agitation. Then he broke into a low laugh, and put his lips to my ear.

'It is a nice household,' he murmured. 'That is the baboon.'

I had forgotten the strange pets which the doctor affected. There was a cheetah, too; perhaps we might find it upon our shoulders at any moment. I confess that I felt easier in my mind when, after following Holmes's example and slipping off my shoes, I found myself inside the bedroom. My companion noiselessly closed the shutters, moved the lamp on to the table, and cast his eyes round the room. All was as we had seen it in the day-time. Then creeping up to me and making a trumpet of his hand, he whispered into my ear again so gently that it was all that I could do to distinguish the words:

'The least sound would be fatal to our plans.'

COMMENTARY

Holmes and Watson watch the lights go out in Helen's house. Then, a couple of hours later, they see Helen's signal and set off for the house. Holmes expects to meet with great danger. They make their way through the grounds and climb into the bedroom through the shutters which have been left open for them.

sombre: dismal
distorted: crippled, misshapen
affected: showed a liking for

I nodded to show that I had heard.

'We must sit without a light. He would see it through the ventilator.'

I nodded again.

'Do not go to sleep; your very life may depend upon it. Have your pistol ready in case we should need it. I will sit on the side of the bed and you in that chair.'

I took out my revolver and laid it on the corner of the table.

Holmes had brought up a long thin cane, and this he placed upon the bed beside him. By it he laid the box of matches and the stump of a candle. Then he turned down the lamp and we were left in darkness.

How shall I ever forget that dreadful vigil? I could not hear a sound, not even the drawing of a breath, and yet I knew that my companion sat open-eyed, within a few feet of me, in the same state of nervous tension in which I was myself. The shutters cut off the least ray of light, and we waited in absolute darkness. From outside came the occasional cry of a night-bird, and once at our very window a long drawn, cat-like whine, which told us that the cheetah was indeed at liberty. Far away we could hear the deep tones of the parish clock, which boomed out every quarter of an hour. How long they seemed, those quarters! Twelve struck, and one, and two, and three, and still we sat waiting silently for whatever might befall.

Suddenly there was the momentary gleam of a light up in the direction of the ventilator, which vanished immediately, but was succeeded by a strong smell of burning oil and heated metal. Someone in the next room had lit a dark lantern. I heard a gentle sound of movement, and then all was silent once more, though the smell grew stronger. For half an hour I sat with straining ears. Then suddenly another sound became audible – a very gentle, soothing sound, like that of a small jet of steam escaping continually from a kettle. The instant that we heard it, Holmes sprang from the bed, struck a match, and lashed furiously with his cane at the bell-pull.

'You see it. Watson?' he yelled. 'You see it?'

But I saw nothing. At the moment when Holmes struck the light I heard a

---

a long thin cane: a long cane walking-stick
vigil: a period spent awake, watching
parish clock: the clock on the parish
  church
befall: happen
dark lantern: a lantern containing a candle,
  but with the sides covered over so that
  very little light would show
became audible: could be heard

COMMENTARY
Holmes whispers to Watson not to make a noise, and not to go to sleep. His life may depend on it. The two men sit in silence for a long time. Suddenly Holmes springs up and lights a match. Watson sees Holmes beating at something on the bell rope with his cane.

low, clear whistle, but the sudden glare flashing into my weary eyes made it impossible for me to tell what it was at which my friend lashed so savagely. I could, however, see that his face was deadly pale, and filled with horror and loathing.

He had ceased to strike, and was gazing up at the ventilator, when suddenly there broke from the silence of the night the most horrible cry to which I have ever listened. It swelled up louder and louder, a hoarse yell of pain and fear and anger all mingled in the one dreadful shriek. They say that away down in the village, and even in the distant parsonage, that cry raised the sleepers from their beds. It struck cold to our hearts, and I stood gazing at Holmes, and he at me, until the last echoes of it had died away into the silence from which it rose.

'What can it mean?' I gasped.

'It means that it is all over,' Holmes answered. 'And perhaps, after all, it is for the best. Take your pistol, and we shall enter Dr Roylott's room.'

With a grave face he lit the lamp, and led the way down the corridor. Twice he struck at the chamber door without any reply from within. Then he turned the handle and entered, I at his heels, with the cocked pistol in my hand.

It was a singular sight which met our eyes. On the table stood a dark lantern with the shutter half open, throwing a brilliant beam of light upon the iron safe, the door of which was ajar. Beside this table, on the wooden chair, sat Dr Grimesby Roylott, clad in a long grey dressing-gown, his bare ankles protruding beneath, and his feet thrust into red heelless Turkish slippers. Across his lap lay the short stock with the long lash which we had noticed during the day. His chin was cocked upwards, and his eyes were fixed in a dreadful rigid stare at the corner of the ceiling. Round his brow he had a peculiar yellow band, with brownish speckles, which seemed to be bound tight round his head. As we entered he made neither sound nor motion.

'The band! the speckled band!' whispered Holmes.

I took a step forward: in an instant his strange headgear began to move, and there reared itself from among his hair the squat diamond-shaped head and puffed neck of a loathsome serpent.

COMMENTARY

Suddenly there is a terrible cry from the room next door. The two men rush in to find Dr Roylott dead, a strange speckled band coiled round his head. The band moves and reveals itself to be a highly poisonous snake.

loathing: hatred
ajar: slightly open
Turkish slippers: exotically embroidered slippers, of a type originally from Turkey
stock: whip handle
serpent: snake

'It is a swamp adder!' cried Holmes – 'the deadliest snake in India. He has died within ten seconds of being bitten. Violence does, in truth, recoil upon the violent, and the schemer falls into the pit which he digs for another. Let us thrust this creature back into its den, and we can then remove Miss Stoner to some place of shelter, and let the county police know what has happened.'

As he spoke he drew the dog whip swiftly from the dead man's lap, and throwing the noose round the reptile's neck, he drew it from its horrid perch, and carrying it at arm's length, threw it into the iron safe, which he closed upon it.

Such are the true facts of the death of Dr Grimesby Roylott, of Stoke Moran. It is not necessary that I should prolong a narrative which has already run to too great a length, by telling how we broke the sad news to the terrified girl, how we conveyed her by the morning train to the care of her good aunt at Harrow, of how the slow process of official inquiry came to the conclusion that the Doctor met his fate while indiscreetly playing with a dangerous pet. The little which I had yet to learn of the case was told me by Sherlock Holmes as we travelled back next day.

'I had,' said he, 'come to an entirely erroneous conclusion, which shows, my dear Watson, how dangerous it always is to reason from insufficient data. The presence of the gipsies, and the use of the word "band", which was used by the poor girl, no doubt, to explain the appearance which she had caught a horrid glimpse of by the light of her match, were sufficient to put me upon an entirely wrong scent. I can only claim the merit that I instantly reconsidered my position when, however, it became clear to me that whatever danger threatened an occupant of the room could not come either from the window or the door. My attention was speedily drawn, as I have already remarked to you, to this ventilator, and to the bell-rope which hung down to the bed. The discovery that this was a dummy, and that the bed was clamped to the floor, instantly gave rise to the suspicion that the rope was there as a bridge for something passing through the hole, and coming to the bed. The idea of a

swamp adder: a snake invented by Conan Doyle – it seems to be a mixture of the Indian cobra and the African puff adder
recoil: turn back
erroneous: wrong

COMMENTARY
Holmes carefully locks the snake away. The two men take Helen to her aunt's, and tell the police what has happened. Holmes talks of the way in which he had at first drawn a false conclusion.

snake instantly occurred to me, and when I coupled it with my knowledge that the Doctor was furnished with a supply of creatures from India, I felt that I was probably on the right track. The idea of using a form of poison which could not possibly be discovered by any chemical test was just such a one as would occur to a clever and ruthless man who had had an Eastern training. The rapidity with which such a poison would take effect would also, from his point of view, be an advantage. It would be a sharp-eyed coroner indeed who could distinguish the two little dark punctures which would show where the poison fangs had done their work. Then I thought of the whistle. Of course, he must recall the snake before the morning light revealed it to the victim. He had trained it, probably by the use of the milk which we saw, to return to him when summoned. He would put it through this ventilator at the hour that he thought best, with the certainty that it would crawl down the rope, and land on the bed. It might or might not bite the occupant, perhaps she might escape every night for a week, but sooner or later she must fall a victim.

'I had come to these conclusions before ever I had entered his room. An inspection of his chair showed me that he had been in the habit of standing on it, which, of course, would be necessary in order that he should reach the ventilator. The sight of the safe, the saucer of milk, and the loop of whipcord were really enough to finally dispel any doubts which may have remained. The metallic clang heard by Miss Stoner was obviously caused by her father hastily closing the door of his safe upon its terrible occupant. Having once made up my mind, you know the steps which I took in order to put the matter to the proof. I heard the creature hiss, as I have no doubt that you did also, and I instantly lit the light and attacked it.'

'With the result of driving it through the ventilator.'

'And also with the result of causing it to turn upon its master at the other side. Some of the blows of my cane came home, and roused its snakish temper, so that it flew upon the first person it saw. In this way I am no doubt indirectly responsible for Dr Grimesby Roylott's death, and I cannot say that it is likely to weigh very heavily upon my conscience.'

COMMENTARY

Holmes takes Watson through the evidence which had led him to expect a snake moving down the bell rope. He finishes by saying that, although he is indirectly to blame for Dr Roylott's death, he cannot bring himself to regret it.

furnished: equipped
rapidity: speed
distinguish: make out
dispel: do away with

Study guide

PLAYBACK QUESTIONS

PAGES 39 TO 52:

➤ 'It is fear, Mr Holmes. It is terror.' (page 41). Why is Helen Stoner so unnerved? From what you have read up to now, do you think her 'terror' is justified, or is she over-reacting?

➤ If you had been the County Coroner, what investigations would you have wanted the police to carry out after Julia's death?

➤ What impressions of Dr Roylott have you formed from his visit to Baker Street (pages 50 and 51)? Are they consistent with Helen's account of him earlier in the story?

➤ Before setting out for Stoke Moran, Holmes tells Watson to make sure he is carrying his revolver. Why might Holmes believe it will be needed? Do you think he is right?

Now return to reading the story on page 52

REVIEWING THE WHOLE STORY: SUGGESTED ACTIVITIES

1 Plotting the murders

Dr Grimesby Roylott plots his stepdaughters' deaths over quite a long period of time. He has clearly put a lot of cunning thought into carrying out the 'perfect murder'.

a   **As a class**, talk about all the things Dr Roylott would have to plan in advance. Make a class list of everything he must have thought about in order to succeed in murdering Julia and Helen – and in getting away with it.

b   **By yourself**, imagine that you are Dr Roylott. You keep a notebook in which you work out how to go about murdering your stepdaughters.

Write entries in your notebook. They should cover every detail of the murder plot, and include all of the following:

● a timetable for action;

● a labelled drawing of the layout of the ground floor at Stoke Moran, showing clearly the corridor and the three bedrooms;

● a list of all the alterations to the house you will need to make if your plot is to work, and of all the things you need to buy;

● anything else you consider important.

2 | Working as a detective

How does Sherlock Holmes set about his detective work?

In Science, when you are given a number of facts which you need to explain, you form a *hypothesis*. This means that you make a guess about what might be the correct explanation for all the facts, then test out your guess to see whether all the facts do actually fit in. If they do, then your hypothesis was correct. If they don't, you need to form another hypothesis – and start all over again!

This is exactly how Sherlock Holmes works when trying to solve a case. He makes observations, collects clues, and then forms a *hypothesis* which might explain them. Sometimes his hypothesis is not correct the first time, so he has to make some new observations until all the facts have been properly accounted for.

a   **With a partner**, scan the story of *The Speckled Band* again. Note down between you the different hypotheses which Holmes forms as the case unfolds, and the clues he uses to back them up.

Which hypothesis does he form first, and why does he need to alter it?

b   **By yourself**, plan and draft a simple mystery story of your own (for example, *The Case of the Missing Milkbottle* or *The Adventure of the Awful Smell,* or something similar). Include in it carefully 'planted' clues which point to a solution or explanation at the end.

Then write your story up, *leaving out* the solution/explanation.

c   Exchange your story with a partner. Each read the other's story. Form a hypothesis to account for the clues in your partner's story, and write it down.

d   Compare *your* hypothesis with your partner's intended solution. See how close it comes to fitting all the facts.

e   **As a class**, you could make a collection of people's Mystery-Stories-Minus-Solutions and keep them in a class book. Swap them around and, as you read them, work out their endings in the way that Sherlock Holmes might do when investigating a case.

3 | News of a death

Looking back over the case of *The Speckled Band*, Watson says that there have been 'widespread rumours' about how and why Dr Roylott died.

a   **In a group**, imagine that you live in a village near Dr Roylott's house at Stoke Moran. Local gossip about the 'strange goings-on at the big house' has been growing for some time.

Look back at the story and pick out all the details which would be likely to give rise to such gossip. They will centre on Dr Roylott's eccentric behaviour (for example, his habit of keeping wild animals, attacking the blacksmith, etc).

Try to come up with between *five* and *eight* 'gossip topics'. If you wish, perform a short role-play in which the villagers share their knowledge and opinions about Dr Roylott ('Always was a funny bloke: a sandwich short of a picnic if you ask me…'/'I heard he's got some sort of a lion wandering round outside his place. My old man swears he saw it last week – nearly fell off his bike, he did…'/'And what about that older girl, Juliet or some such fancy name. Haven't seen her for a bit, have we?').

b   **By yourself**, write two newspaper reports of the events at Stoke Moran as they would be presented to the public *after Dr Roylott's death*.

  (i)   The first appears in the local paper. The reporter will know more or less exactly what happened, including the names and characters of everyone involved.

  (ii) The second is written for one of the more lurid 'tabloid' newspapers, which sells its stories through sensational descriptions (and/or rumours) of violence, intrigue and sleaze. In writing *this* report, you can be as imaginative as you like!

Each report will be printed as front page. Present and set them out in a suitable way with headlines, columns, illustrations, etc. Use a computer if you wish. Finally, contribute them to a **class display**.

LOCAL MAN DIES

Surrey wild man in death horror sensation!

THE DANCING MEN

Look out for...
- **Mrs Hilton Cubitt. What impressions do you get of her?**
- **the way in which Holmes solves the case on his own, without sharing his ideas with anyone. Why do you think he does not keep Watson informed as he goes along?**

Holmes had been seated for some hours in silence with his long, thin back curved over a chemical vessel in which he was brewing a particularly malodorous product. His head was sunk upon his breast, and he looked from my point of view like a strange, lank bird, with dull grey plumage and a black top-knot.

'So, Watson,' said he, suddenly, 'you do not propose to invest in South African securities?'

I gave a start of astonishment. Accustomed as I was to Holmes's curious faculties, this sudden intrusion into my most intimate thoughts was utterly inexplicable.

'How on earth do you know that?' I asked.

He wheeled round upon his stool, with a steaming test-tube in his hand and a gleam of amusement in his deep-set eyes.

'Now, Watson, confess yourself utterly taken aback,' said he.

'I am.'

'I ought to make you sign a paper to that effect.'

COMMENTARY
Holmes and Watson are sitting together in the flat which they share, when Holmes startles Watson by apparently reading his mind.

vessel: container
malodorous: smelly
securities: loans made against property
faculties: mental powers
confess: admit

'Why?'

'Because in five minutes you will say that it's all so absurdly simple.'

'I am sure that I shall say nothing of the kind.'

'You see, my dear Watson' – he propped his test-tube in the rack and began to lecture with the air of a professor addressing his class – 'it is not really difficult to construct a series of inferences, each dependent upon its predecessor and each simple in itself. If, after doing so, one simply knocks out all the central inferences and presents one's audience with the starting-point and the conclusion, one may produce a startling, though possibly a meretricious, effect. Now, it was not really difficult, by an inspection of the groove between your left forefinger and thumb, to feel sure that you did *not* propose to invest your small capital in the goldfields.'

'I see no connection.'

'Very likely not; but I can quickly show you a close connection. Here are the missing links of the very simple chain: 1. You had chalk between your left finger and thumb when you returned from the club last night. 2. You put chalk there when you play billiards to steady the cue. 3. You never play billiards except with Thurston. 4. You told me four weeks ago that Thurston had an option on some South African property which would expire in a month, and which he desired you to share with him. 5. Your cheque-book is locked in my drawer, and you have not asked for the key. 6. You do not propose to invest your money in this manner.'

'How absurdly simple!' I cried.

'Quite so!' said he, a little nettled. 'Every problem becomes very childish when once it is explained to you. Here is an unexplained one. See what you can make of that, friend Watson.' He tossed a sheet of paper upon the table and turned once more to his chemical analysis.

I looked with amazement at the absurd hieroglyphics upon the paper.

'Why, Holmes, it is a child's drawing!' I cried.

'Oh, that's your idea!'

'What else should it be?'

---

inferences: deductions, guesses based on a
   series of known facts
predecessor: the one that went before
meretricious: showy
option: the opportunity to buy
nettled: irritated
hieroglyphics: pictures standing for words
   or ideas; signs, symbols

COMMENTARY

Holmes explains how he was able to use a series of facts which he knew about Watson's life and habits to work out what he had been thinking. Holmes then asks Watson's opinion about a line of drawings on a piece of paper which he throws over to him. Watson says he thinks it looks like a child's drawing.

'That is what Mr Hilton Cubitt, of Ridling Thorpe Manor, Norfolk, is very anxious to know. This little conundrum came by the first post, and he was to follow by the next train. There's a ring at the bell, Watson. I should not be very much surprised if this were he.'

A heavy step was heard upon the stairs, and an instant later there appeared a tall, ruddy, clean-shaven gentleman, whose clear eyes and florid cheeks told of a life led far from the fogs of Baker Street. He seemed to bring a whiff of his strong, fresh, bracing, east-coast air with him as he entered. Having shaken hands with each of us, he was about to sit down, when his eye rested upon the paper with the curious markings, which I had just examined and left upon the table.

'Well, Mr Holmes, what do you make of these?' he cried. 'They told me that you were fond of queer mysteries, and I don't think you can find a queerer one than that. I sent the paper on ahead so that you might have time to study it before I came.'

'It is certainly rather a curious production,' said Holmes. 'At first sight it would appear to be some childish prank. It consists of a number of absurd little figures dancing across the paper upon which they are drawn. Why should you attribute any importance to so grotesque an object?'

'I never should, Mr Holmes. But my wife does. It is frightening her to death. She says nothing, but I can see terror in her eyes. That's why I want to sift the matter to the bottom.'

Holmes held up the paper so that the sunlight shone full upon it. It was a page torn from a notebook. The markings were done in pencil, and ran in this way:

COMMENTARY

The man who has sent the drawing arrives. He is called Hilton Cubitt. He asks Holmes whether he has been able to make sense of the drawing. He explains that there is something in it which is terrifying his wife.

conundrum: puzzle
florid: ruddy, rosy
attribute: attach
sift: explore, investigate

Holmes examined it for some time, and then, folding it carefully up, he placed it in his pocket-book.

'This promises to be a most interesting and unusual case,' said he. 'You gave me a few particulars in your letter, Mr Hilton Cubitt, but I should be very much obliged if you would kindly go over it all again for the benefit of my friend, Dr Watson.'

'I'm not much of a story-teller,' said our visitor, nervously clasping and unclasping his great, strong hands. 'You'll just ask me anything that I don't make clear. I'll begin at the time of my marriage last year; but I want to say first of all that, though I'm not a rich man, my people have been at Ridling Thorpe for a matter of five centuries, and there is no better known family in the county of Norfolk. Last year I came up to London for the Jubilee, and I stopped at a boarding-house in Russell Square, because Parker, the vicar of our parish, was staying in it. There was an American young lady there – Patrick was the name – Elsie Patrick. In some way we became friends, until before my month was up I was as much in love as a man could be. We were quietly married at a registry office, and we returned to Norfolk a wedded couple. You'll think it very mad, Mr Holmes, that a man of a good old family should marry a wife in this fashion, knowing nothing of her past or her people; but if you saw her and knew her it would help you to understand.

'She was very straight about it, was Elsie. I can't say that she did not give me every chance of getting out of it if I wished to do so. "I have had some very disagreeable associations in my life," said she; "I wish to forget all about them. I would rather never allude to the past, for it is very painful to me. If you take me, Hilton, you will take a woman who has nothing that she need be personally ashamed of; but you will have to be content with my word for it, and to allow me to be silent as to all that passed up to the time when I became yours. If these conditions are too hard, then go back to Norfolk and leave me to the lonely life in which you found me." It was only the day before our wedding that she said those very words to me. I told her that I was content to take her on her own terms, and I have been as good as my word.

COMMENTARY

Holmes looks at the paper carefully and asks Cubitt to explain the background to the case.

Cubitt explains how he met and married his wife, an American woman, and how they now live at his family home in Norfolk. Before they were married, his wife, Elsie, told him that there was a shameful secret in her past, although she had never done anything to be ashamed of herself. Cubitt decided to marry her all the same.

Jubilee: a celebration held in 1897 to mark the fact that Queen Victoria had been on the throne for 50 years

straight: honest
allude: refer back

'Well, we have been married now for a year, and very happy we have been. But about a month ago, at the end of June, I saw for the first time signs of trouble. One day my wife received a letter from America. I saw the American stamp. She turned deadly white, read the letter, and threw it into the fire. She made no allusion to it afterwards, and I made none, for a promise is a promise; but she has never known an easy hour from that moment. There is always a look of fear upon her face – a look as if she were waiting and expecting. She would do better to trust me. She would find that I was her best friend. But until she speaks I can say nothing. Mind you, she is a truthful woman, Mr Holmes, and whatever trouble there has been in her past life, it has been no fault of hers. I am only a simple Norfolk squire, but there is not a man in England who ranks his family honour more highly than I do. She knows it well, and she knew it well before she married me. She would never bring any stain upon it – of that I am sure.

'Well, now I come to the queer part of my story. About a week ago – it was the Tuesday of last week – I found on one of the window-sills a number of absurd little dancing figures, like these upon the paper. They were scrawled with chalk. I thought that it was the stable-boy who had drawn them, but the lad swore he knew nothing about it. Anyhow, they had come there during the night. I had them washed out, and I only mentioned the matter to my wife afterwards. To my surprise she took it very seriously, and begged me if any more came to let her see them. None did come for a week, and then yesterday morning I found this paper lying on the sun-dial in the garden. I showed it to Elsie, and down she dropped in a dead faint. Since then she has looked like a woman in a dream, half dazed, and with terror always lurking in her eyes. It was then that I wrote and sent the paper to you, Mr Holmes. It was not a thing that I could take to the police, for they would have laughed at me, but you will tell me what to do. I am not a rich man; but if there is any danger threatening my little woman, I would spend my last copper to shield her.'

He was a fine creature, this man of the old English soil, simple, straight, and gentle, with his great, earnest blue eyes and broad, comely face. His love for

COMMENTARY
The Cubitts were very happy together, until about a month ago Elsie received a letter from America, which clearly worried her. Later, a series of childish drawings appeared on a window-sill at Cubitt's house. He thought it was a prank, and had them cleaned off, but when he told his wife she was very troubled. Hence he has come to Holmes for help.

allusion: reference
queer: odd, puzzling
copper: old penny
comely: handsome

his wife and his trust in her shone in his features. Holmes had listened to his story with the utmost attention, and now he sat for some time in silent thought.

'Don't you think, Mr Cubitt,' said he at last, 'that your best plan would be to make a direct appeal to your wife, and to ask her to share her secret with you?'

Hilton Cubitt shook his massive head.

'A promise is a promise, Mr Holmes. If Elsie wished to tell me, she would. If not, it is not for me to force her confidence. But I am justified in taking my own line – and I will.'

'Then I will help you with all my heart. In the first place, have you heard of any strangers being seen in your neighbourhood?'

'No.'

'I presume that it is a very quiet place. Any fresh face would cause comment?'

'In the immediate neighbourhood, yes. But we have several small watering-places not very far away. And the farmers take in lodgers.'

'These hieroglyphics have evidently a meaning. If it is a purely arbitrary one, it may be impossible for us to solve it. If, on the other hand, it is systematic, I have no doubt that we shall get to the bottom of it. But this particular sample is so short that I can do nothing, and the facts which you have brought me are so indefinite that we have no basis for an investigation. I would suggest that you return to Norfolk, that you keep a keen look-out, and that you take an exact copy of any fresh dancing men which may appear. It is a thousand pities that we have not a reproduction of those which were done in chalk upon the window-sill. Make a discreet inquiry, also, as to any strangers in the neighbourhood. When you have collected some fresh evidence, come to me again. That is the best advice which I can give you, Mr Hilton Cubitt. If there are any pressing fresh developments, I shall be always ready to run down and see you in your Norfolk home.'

The interview left Sherlock Holmes very thoughtful, and several times in the next few days I saw him take his slip of paper from his note-book and look

force her confidence: make her reveal her
   secrets
watering-places: seaside resorts
arbitrary: not based on a regular system;
   random
indefinite: vague, uncertain

COMMENTARY
Holmes begins to question Cubitt. He tries to find out whether there are any strangers in the neighbourhood. Cubitt does not know, but thinks it possible. Holmes recommends that he returns home, and says that he will travel down to Norfolk if anything more occurs.

long and earnestly at the curious figures inscribed upon it. He made no allusion to the affair, however, until one afternoon a fortnight or so later. I was going out when he called me back.

'You had better stay here, Watson.'

'Why?'

'Because I had a wire from Hilton Cubitt this morning – you remember Hilton Cubitt, of the dancing men? He was to reach Liverpool Street at one-twenty. He may be here at any moment. I gather from his wire that there have been some new incidents of some importance.'

We had not long to wait, for our Norfolk squire came straight from the station as fast as a hansom could bring him. He was looking worried and depressed, with tired eyes and a lined forehead.

'It's getting on my nerves, this business, Mr Holmes,' said he, as he sank, like a wearied man, into an arm-chair. 'It's bad enough to feel that you are surrounded by unseen, unknown folk who have some kind of design upon you; but when, in addition to that, you know that it is just killing your wife by inches, then it becomes as much as flesh and blood can endure. She's wearing away under it – just wearing away before my eyes.'

'Has she said anything yet?'

'No, Mr Holmes, she has not. And yet there have been times when the poor girl has wanted to speak, and yet could not quite bring herself to take the plunge. I have tried to help her; but I dare say I did it clumsily, and scared her off from it. She has spoken about my old family, and our reputation in the county, and our pride in our unsullied honour, and I always felt it was leading to the point; but somehow it turned off before we got there.'

'But you have found out something yourself?'

'A good deal, Mr Holmes. I have several fresh dancing men pictures for you to examine, and, what is more important, I have seen the fellow.'

'What – the man who draws them?'

'Yes, I saw him at his work. But I will tell you everything in order. When I got back after my visit to you, the very first thing I saw next morning was a

COMMENTARY

A few days later Holmes tells Watson that Cubitt will be calling to tell Holmes of more developments in the case. When Hilton Cubitt arrives, he tells Holmes that his wife is growing more worried. There have been more drawings, and Cubitt has even seen the man who is doing them.

wire: telegraph message
Liverpool Street: a main-line London station
hansom: a two-wheeled, horse-drawn cab
design: plot
unsullied: pure, unstained

fresh crop of dancing men. They had been drawn in chalk upon the black wooden door of the tool-house, which stands beside the lawn in full view of the front windows. I took an exact copy, and here it is.' He unfolded a paper and laid it upon the table. Here is a copy of the hieroglyphics:

'Excellent!' said Holmes. 'Excellent! Pray continue.'
'When I had taken the copy I rubbed out the marks; but two mornings later a fresh inscription had appeared. I have a copy of it here':

Holmes rubbed his hands and chuckled with delight.
'Our material is rapidly accumulating,' said he.
'Three days later a message was left scrawled upon paper, and placed under a pebble upon the sun-dial. Here it is. The characters are, as you see, exactly the same as the last one. After that I determined to lie in wait; so I got out my revolver and I sat up in my study, which overlooks the lawn and garden. About two in the morning I was seated by the window, all being dark save for the moonlight outside, when I heard steps behind me, and there was my wife in her

accumulating: increasing, growing
sun-dial: an old-fashioned way for showing the time of day by means of a shadow cast by the sun upon a surface marked with a diagram indicating the hours, usually made of stone or metal

COMMENTARY
Cubitt passes to Holmes copies of the latest drawings to appear, and explains how his wife found him lying in wait for the person who had done them.

dressing-gown. She implored me to come to bed. I told her frankly that I wished to see who it was who played such absurd tricks upon us. She answered that it was some senseless practical joke, and that I should not take any notice of it.

"'If it really annoys you, Hilton, we might go and travel, you and I, and so avoid this nuisance.'

"'What, be driven out of our own house by a practical joker?' said I. 'Why, we should have the whole county laughing at us.'

"'Well, come to bed,' said she, 'and we can discuss it in the morning.'

'Suddenly, as she spoke, I saw her white face grow whiter yet in the moonlight, and her hand tightened upon my shoulder. Something was moving in the shadow of the tool-house. I saw a dark, creeping figure which crawled round the corner and squatted in front of the door. Seizing my pistol I was rushing out, when my wife threw her arms round me and held me with convulsive strength. I tried to throw her off, but she clung to me most desperately. At last I got clear, but by the time I had opened the door and reached the house the creature was gone. He had left a trace of his presence, however, for there on the door was the very same arrangement of dancing men which had already twice appeared, and which I have copied on that paper. There was no other sign of the fellow anywhere, though I ran all over the grounds. And yet the amazing thing is that he must have been there all the time, for when I examined the door again in the morning he had scrawled some more of his pictures under the line which I had already seen.'

'Have you that fresh drawing?'

'Yes; it is very short, but I made a copy of it, and here it is.'

Again he produced a paper. The new dance was in this form:

COMMENTARY

Elsie Cubitt suggests that they might go away for a while to escape this annoyance. Cubitt refuses to think of running away. Just then he catches sight of the man who is doing the drawings, and is about to go after him when his wife restrains him. After that night, though, more drawings have appeared, copies of which he passes to Holmes.

implored: begged
convulsive: sudden and violent

'Tell me,' said Holmes – and I could see by his eyes that he was much excited – 'was this a mere addition to the first, or did it appear to be entirely separate?'

'It was on a different panel of the door.'

'Excellent! This is far the most important of all for our purpose. It fills me with hopes. Now, Mr Hilton Cubitt, please continue your most interesting statement.'

'I have nothing more to say, Mr Holmes, except that I was angry with my wife that night for having held me back when I might have caught the skulking rascal. She said that she feared that I might come to harm. For an instant it had crossed my mind that perhaps what she really feared was that *he* might come to harm, for I could not doubt that she knew who this man was and what he meant by these strange signals. But there is a tone in my wife's voice, Mr Holmes, and a look in her eyes which forbid doubt, and I am sure that it was indeed my own safety that was in her mind. There's the whole case, and now I want your advice as to what I ought to do. My own inclination is to put half-a-dozen of my farm lads in the shrubbery, and when this fellow comes again to give him such a hiding that he will leave us in peace for the future.'

'I fear it is too deep a case for such simple remedies,' said Holmes. 'How long can you stay in London?'

'I must go back to-day. I would not leave my wife alone at night for anything. She is very nervous and begged me to come back.'

'I dare say you are right. But if you could have stopped I might possibly have been able to return with you in a day or two. Meanwhile, you will leave me these papers, and I think that it is very likely that I shall be able to pay you a visit shortly and to throw some light upon your case.'

Sherlock Holmes preserved his calm professional manner until our visitor had left us, although it was easy for me, who knew him so well, to see that he was profoundly excited. The moment that Hilton Cubitt's broad back had disappeared through the door my comrade rushed to the table, laid out all the slips of paper containing dancing men in front of him, and threw himself into an intricate and elaborate calculation.

skulking: sneaking, lurking
hiding: beating
deep: serious, dangerous
remedies: solutions
profoundly: extremely
intricate: complicated

COMMENTARY
Holmes asks Cubitt if he can stay while he tries to unravel the case, but Cubitt says he must get back to his wife, as she is so frightened. He leaves, and Holmes settles down to solving the puzzle of the drawings.

For two hours I watched him as he covered sheet after sheet of paper with figures and letters, so completely absorbed in his task that he had evidently forgotten my presence. Sometimes he was making progress, and whistled and sang at his work; sometimes he was puzzled, and would sit for a long spell with a furrowed brow and a vacant eye. Finally he sprang from his chair with a cry of satisfaction, and walked up and down the room rubbing his hands together. Then he wrote a long telegram upon a cable form. 'If my answer to this is as I hope, you will have a very pretty case to add to your collection, Watson,' said he. 'I expect that we shall be able to go down to Norfolk to-morrow, and to take our friend some very definite news as to the secret of his annoyance.'

I confess that I was filled with curiosity, but I was aware that Holmes liked to make his disclosures at his own time and in his own way; so I waited until it should suit him to take me into his confidence.

But there was a delay in that answering telegram, and two days of impatience followed, during which Holmes pricked up his ears at every ring of the bell. On the evening of the second there came a letter from Hilton Cubitt. All was quiet with him, save that a long inscription had appeared that morning upon the pedestal of the sun-dial. He enclosed a copy of it, which is here reproduced:

Holmes bent over this grotesque frieze for some minutes and then suddenly sprang to his feet with an exclamation of surprise and dismay. His face was haggard with anxiety.

COMMENTARY

Holmes works hard to crack what seems to be a code, and eventually manages to do it. He sends a telegram to find out some additional facts, and receives a letter from Hilton Cubitt with a copy of yet another series of drawings. Holmes is alarmed at what this latest series of drawings reveals, and is now eager to hurry down to Norfolk.

furrowed: wrinkled
telegram: a message sent by telegraph, an electronic communications device
cable form: a form on which to write a telegram
make his disclosures: tell his account
inscription: a piece of writing or drawing on a wall or other surface
frieze: line of drawings
haggard: white, worn-out

'We have let this affair go far enough,' said he. 'Is there a train to North Walsham to-night?'

I turned up the time-table. The last had just gone.

'Then we shall breakfast early and take the very first in the morning,' said Holmes. 'Our presence is most urgently needed. Ah! here is our expected cablegram. One moment, Mrs Hudson – there may be an answer. No, that is quite as I expected. This message makes it even more essential that we should not lose an hour in letting Hilton Cubitt know how matters stand, for it is a singular and a dangerous web in which our simple Norfolk squire is entangled.'

So, indeed, it proved, and as I come to the dark conclusion of a story which had seemed to me to be only childish and bizarre I experience once again the dismay and horror with which I was filled. Would that I had some brighter ending to communicate to my readers; but these are the chronicles of facts, and I must follow to their dark crisis the strange chain of events which for some days made Ridling Thorpe Manor a household word through the length and breadth of England.

We had hardly alighted at North Walsham, and mentioned the name of our destination, when the station-master hurried towards us. 'I suppose that you are the detectives from London?' said he.

A look of annoyance passed over Holmes's face.

'What makes you think such a thing?'

'Because Inspector Martin from Norwich has just passed through. But maybe you are the surgeons. She's not dead – or wasn't by last accounts. You may be in time to save her yet – though it be for the gallows.'

Holmes's brow was dark with anxiety.

'We are going to Ridling Thorpe Manor,' said he, 'but we have heard nothing of what has passed there.'

'It's a terrible business,' said the station-master. 'They are shot, both Mr Hilton Cubitt and his wife. She shot him and then herself – so the servants say. He's dead and her life is despaired of. Dear, dear! one of the oldest families

---

COMMENTARY

The last train to Norfolk has gone, so Holmes and Watson go down by the first train the next morning. They are surprised by the station-master greeting them as the detectives from London, and saying that Mrs Cubitt is near to death and suspected of murder. Holmes explains that he and Watson know nothing of what has happened at the Cubitt house during the night. The station-master tells them that Hilton Cubitt is dead and his wife badly wounded. It is assumed that she shot him and then herself.

---

turned up: looked up
singular: strange, unusual
bizarre: strange, extraordinary
alighted: got off the train

gallows: an apparatus used for inflicting death by hanging – the victim is suspended by the neck from the crosspiece

in the county of Norfolk, and one of the most honoured.'

Without a word Holmes hurried to a carriage, and during the long, seven-miles drive he never opened his mouth. Seldom have I seen him so utterly despondent. He had been uneasy during all our journey from town, and I had observed that he had turned over the morning papers with anxious attention; but now this sudden realisation of his worst fears left him in a blank melancholy. He leaned back in his seat, lost in gloomy speculation. Yet there was much around us to interest us, for we were passing through as singular a countryside as any in England, where a few scattered cottages represented the population of to-day, while on every hand enormous square-towered churches bristled up from the flat, green landscape and told of the glory and prosperity of old East Anglia. At last the violet rim of the German Ocean appeared over the green edge of the Norfolk coast, and the driver pointed with his whip to two old brick and timber gables which projected from a grove of trees. 'That's Ridling Thorpe Manor,' said he.

As we drove up to the porticoed front door, I observed in front of it, beside the tennis lawn, the black tool-house and the pedestalled sun-dial with which we had such strange associations. A dapper little man, with a quick, alert manner and a waxed moustache, had just descended from a high dog-cart. He introduced himself as Inspector Martin, of the Norfolk Constabulary, and he was considerably astonished when he heard the name of my companion.

'Why, Mr Holmes, the crime was only committed at three this morning! How could you hear of it in London and get to the spot as soon as I?'

'I anticipated it. I came in the hope of preventing it.'

'Then you must have important evidence of which we are ignorant, for they were said to be a most united couple.'

'I have only the evidence of the dancing men,' said Holmes. 'I will explain the matter to you later. Meanwhile, since it is too late to prevent this tragedy, I am very anxious that I should use the knowledge which I possess in order to ensure that justice be done. Will you associate me in your investigation, or will you prefer that I should act independently?'

COMMENTARY

Holmes is deeply upset by the news, and he and Watson hurry to the house, where they meet the police inspector in charge of the case. Inspector Martin is astonished to see them on the spot so promptly, especially when Holmes explains that he had hoped to arrive in time to prevent the crime.

despondent: depressed
melancholy: deep sadness
German Ocean: North Sea
porticoed front door: a front door with a roofed porch over it – the roof is often supported by columns
dapper: stylish, smart
dog-cart: a small open horse-drawn carriage
associate me: officially include me

'I should be proud to feel that we were acting together, Mr Holmes,' said the inspector earnestly.

'In that case I should be glad to hear the evidence and to examine the premises without an instant of unnecessary delay.'

Inspector Martin had the good sense to allow my friend to do things in his own fashion, and contented himself with carefully noting the results. The local surgeon, an old, white-haired man, had just come down from Mrs Hilton Cubitt's room, and he reported that her injuries were serious, but not necessarily fatal. The bullet had passed through the front of her brain, and it would probably be some time before she could regain consciousness. On the question of whether she had been shot or had shot herself he would not venture to express any decided opinion. Certainly the bullet had been discharged at very close quarters. There was only the one pistol found in the room, two barrels of which had been emptied. Mr Hilton Cubitt had been shot through the heart. It was equally conceivable that he had shot her and then himself, or that she had been the criminal, for the revolver lay upon the floor midway between them.

'Has he been moved?' asked Holmes.

'We have moved nothing except the lady. We could not leave her lying wounded upon the floor.'

'How long have you been here, doctor?'

'Since four o'clock.'

'Anyone else?'

'Yes, the constable here.'

'And you have touched nothing?'

'Nothing.'

'You have acted with great discretion. Who sent for you?'

'The housemaid, Saunders.'

'Was it she who gave the alarm?'

'She and Mrs King, the cook.'

'Where are they now?'

'In the kitchen, I believe.'

discharged: fired
conceivable: possible

COMMENTARY

As Holmes and Inspector Martin each have facts about the case, they decide to pool their knowledge and work together. Holmes questions the doctor who has examined Mrs Cubitt and the body of Hilton Cubitt.

'Then I think we had better hear their story at once.'

The old hall, oak-panelled and high-windowed, had been turned into a court of investigation. Holmes sat in a great, old-fashioned chair, his inexorable eyes gleaming out of his haggard face. I could read in them a set purpose to devote his life to this quest until the client whom he had failed to save should at last be avenged. The trim Inspector Martin, the old, grey-headed country doctor, myself, and a stolid village policeman made up the rest of that strange company.

The two women told their story clearly enough. They had been aroused from their sleep by the sound of an explosion, which had been followed a minute later by a second one. They slept in adjoining rooms, and Mrs King had rushed in to Saunders. Together they had descended the stairs. The door of the study was open and a candle was burning upon the table. Their master lay upon his face in the centre of the room. He was quite dead. Near the window his wife was crouching, her head leaning against the wall. She was horribly wounded, and the side of her face was red with blood. She breathed heavily, but was incapable of saying anything. The passage, as well as the room, was full of smoke and the smell of powder. The window was certainly shut and fastened upon the inside. Both women were positive upon the point. They had at once sent for the doctor and for the constable. Then, with the aid of the groom and the stable-boy, they had conveyed their injured mistress to her room. Both she and her husband had occupied the bed. She was clad in her dress – he in his dressing-gown, over his night-clothes. Nothing had been moved in the study. So far as they knew, there had never been any quarrel between husband and wife. They had always looked upon them as a very united couple.

These were the main points of the servants' evidence. In answer to Inspector Martin they were clear that every door was fastened upon the inside, and that no one could have escaped from the house. In answer to Holmes, they both remembered that they were conscious of the smell of powder from the moment that they ran out of their rooms on the top floor. 'I commend that

COMMENTARY
Holmes listens to the stories of the two servants who discovered the bodies.

inexorable: determined, fixed
quest: search
powder: gunpowder

fact very carefully to your attention,' said Holmes to his professional colleague. 'And now I think that we are in a position to undertake a thorough examination of the room.'

The study proved to be a small chamber, lined on three sides with books, and with a writing-table facing an ordinary window, which looked out upon the garden. Our first attention was given to the body of the unfortunate squire, whose huge frame lay stretched across the room. His disordered dress showed that he had been hastily aroused from sleep. The bullet had been fired at him from the front, and had remained in his body after penetrating the heart. His death had certainly been instantaneous and painless. There was no powder-marking either upon his dressing-gown or on his hands. According to the country surgeon the lady had stains upon her face, but none upon her hand.

'The absence of the latter means nothing, though its presence may mean everything,' said Holmes. 'Unless the powder from a badly fitting cartridge happens to spurt backwards, one may fire many shots without leaving a sign. I would suggest that Mr Cubitt's body may now be removed. I suppose, doctor, that you have not recovered the bullet which wounded the lady?'

'A serious operation will be necessary before that can be done. But there are still four cartridges in the revolver. Two have been fired and two wounds inflicted, so that each bullet can be accounted for.'

'So it would seem,' said Holmes. 'Perhaps you can account also for the bullet which has so obviously struck the edge of the window?'

He had turned suddenly, and his long, thin finger was pointing to a hole which had been drilled right through the lower window-sash about an inch above the bottom.

'By George!' cried the inspector. 'How ever did you see that?'

'Because I looked for it.'

'Wonderful!' said the country doctor. 'You are certainly right, sir. Then a third shot has been fired, and therefore a third person must have been present. But who could that have been and how could he have got away?'

'That is the problem which we are now about to solve,' said Sherlock

chamber: room
penetrating: entering
instantaneous: immediate

COMMENTARY
Holmes now decides to examine the scene of the crime. He checks the room carefully and finds evidence of a third shot having been fired.

Holmes. 'You remember, Inspector Martin, when the servants said that on leaving their room they were at once conscious of a smell of powder, I remarked that the point was an extremely important one?'

'Yes, sir, but I confess I did not quite follow you.'

'It suggested that at the time of the firing the window as well as the door of the room had been open. Otherwise the fumes of powder could not have been blown so rapidly through the house. A draught in the room was necessary for that. Both door and window were only open for a short time, however.'

'How do you prove that?'

'Because the candle has not guttered.'

'Capital!' cried the inspector. 'Capital!'

'Feeling sure that the window had been open at the time of the tragedy, I conceived that there might have been a third person in the affair, who stood outside this opening and fired through it. Any shot directed at this person might hit the sash. I looked, and there, sure enough, was the bullet mark!'

'But how came the window to be shut and fastened?'

'The woman's first instinct would be to shut and fasten the window. But, hullo! what is this?'

It was a lady's hand-bag which stood upon the study table – a trim little hand-bag of crocodile-skin and silver. Holmes opened it and turned the contents out. There were twenty fifty-pound notes of the Bank of England, held together by an India-rubber band – nothing else.

'This must be preserved, for it will figure in the trial,' said Holmes, as he handed the bag with its contents to the inspector. 'It is now necessary that we should try to throw some light upon this third bullet, which has clearly, from the splintering of the wood, been fired from inside the room. I should like to see Mrs King, the cook, again…You said, Mrs King, that you were awakened by a *loud* explosion. When you said that, did you mean that it seemed to you to be louder than the second one?'

'Well, sir, it wakened me from my sleep, and so it is hard to judge. But it did seem very loud.'

guttered: flickered. The flame had not been blown about, causing the wax to burn unevenly
Capital!: excellent!
conceived: imagined

'You don't think that it might have been two shots fired almost at the same instant?'

'I am sure I couldn't say, sir.'

'I believe that it was undoubtedly so. I rather think, Inspector Martin, that we have now exhausted all that this room can teach us. If you will kindly step round with me we shall see what fresh evidence the garden has to offer.'

A flower-bed extended up to the study window, and we all broke into an exclamation as we approached it. The flowers were trampled down, and the soft soil was imprinted all over with footmarks. Large, masculine feet they were, with peculiarly long, sharp toes. Holmes hunted about among the grass and leaves like a retriever after a wounded bird. Then, with a cry of satisfaction, he bent forward and picked up a little brazen cylinder.

'I thought so,' said he; 'the revolver had an ejector, and here is the third cartridge. I really think, Inspector Martin, that our case is almost complete.'

The country inspector's face had shown his intense amazement at the rapid and masterful progress of Holmes's investigations. At first he had shown some disposition to assert his own position; but now he was overcome with admiration, and ready to follow without question wherever Holmes led.

'Whom do you suspect?' he asked.

'I'll go into that later. There are several points in this problem which I have not been able to explain to you yet. Now that I have got so far I had best proceed on my own lines, and then clear the whole matter up once and for all.'

'Just as you wish, Mr Holmes, so long as we get our man.'

'I have no desire to make mysteries, but it is impossible at the moment of action to enter into long and complex explanations. I have the threads of this affair all in my hand. Even if this lady should never recover consciousness we can still reconstruct the events of last night and ensure that justice be done. First of all I wish to know whether there is any inn in this neighbourhood known as "Elrige's"?'

peculiarly: unusually
brazen: made of brass
disposition: wish

COMMENTARY

Holmes finds footprints and a cartridge case outside the window, which show that somebody had stood outside the window and fired into the room. Inspector Martin agrees to let Holmes proceed with the inquiry in his own way for the time being. Holmes asks if there is an inn called Elrige's near by.

The servants were cross-questioned, but none of them had heard of such a place. The stable-boy threw a light upon the matter by remembering that a farmer of that name lived some miles off in the direction of East Ruston.

'Is it a lonely farm?'

'Very lonely, sir.'

'Perhaps they have not heard yet of all that happened here during the night?'

'Maybe not, sir.'

Holmes thought for a little and then a curious smile played over his face.

'Saddle a horse, my lad,' said he. 'I shall wish you to take a note to Elrige's Farm.'

He took from his pocket the various slips of the dancing men. With these in front of him he worked for some time at the study-table. Finally he handed a note to the boy, with directions to put it into the hands of the person to whom it was addressed, and especially to answer no questions of any sort which might be put to him. I saw the outside of the note, addressed in straggling, irregular characters, very unlike Holmes's usual precise hand. It was consigned to Mr Abe Slaney, Elrige's Farm, East Ruston, Norfolk.

'I think, Inspector,' Holmes remarked, 'that you would do well to telegraph for an escort, as, if my calculations prove to be correct, you may have a particularly dangerous prisoner to convey to the county gaol. The boy who takes this note could no doubt forward your telegram. If there is an afternoon train to town, Watson, I think we should do well to take it, as I have a chemical analysis of some interest to finish, and this investigation draws rapidly to a close.'

PAUSE FOR PLAYBACK:
Now look at the playback questions on page 99 before going on with your reading.

COMMENTARY
The stable boy remembers that there is a farm called Elrige's some miles away. Holmes writes a note for him to take to a man there.

characters: letters
precise hand: neat handwriting
consigned: addressed
escort: assistant

When the youth had been dispatched with the note, Sherlock Holmes gave his instructions to the servants. If any visitor were to call asking for Mrs Hilton Cubitt no information should be given as to her condition, but he was to be shown at once into the drawing-room. He impressed these points upon them with the utmost earnestness. Finally he led the way into the drawing-room, with the remark that the business was now out of our hands, and that we must while away the time as best we might until we could see what was in store for us. The doctor had departed to his patients, and only the inspector and myself remained.

'I think I can help you to pass an hour in an interesting and profitable manner,' said Holmes, drawing his chair up to the table and spreading out in front of him the various papers upon which were recorded the antics of the dancing men. 'As to you, friend Watson, I owe you every atonement for having allowed your natural curiosity to remain so long unsatisfied. To you, inspector, the whole incident may appeal as a remarkable professional study. I must tell you first of all the interesting circumstances connected with the previous consultations which Mr Hilton Cubitt has had with me in Baker Street.' He then shortly recapitulated the facts which have already been recorded.

'I have here in front of me these singular productions, at which one might smile had they not proved themselves to be the forerunners of so terrible a tragedy. I am fairly familiar with all forms of secret writings, and am myself the author of a trifling monograph upon the subject, in which I analyse one hundred and sixty separate ciphers; but I confess that this is entirely new to me. The object of those who invented the system has apparently been to conceal that these characters convey a message, and to give the idea that they are the mere random sketches of children.

'Having once recognised, however, that the symbols stood for letters, and having applied the rules which guide us in all forms of secret writings, the solution was easy enough. The first message submitted to me was so short that it was impossible for me to do more than say with some confidence that the symbol 𝑋 stood for E. As you are aware, E is the most common letter in the English alphabet and it predominates to so marked an extent that even

---

dispatched: sent off
I owe you every atonement: I must make it
  up to you
recapitulated: went back over
trifling monograph: a simple article
ciphers: characters
predominates to so marked an extent: is
  used so much more than other letters

COMMENTARY
While Holmes, Watson and the Inspector wait for the results of the note which Holmes has sent, Holmes explains how he solved the code of the dancing men.

in a short sentence one would expect to find it most often. Out of fifteen symbols in the first message four were the same, so it was reasonable to set this down as E. It is true that in some cases the figure was bearing a flag and in some cases not, but it was probable from the way in which the flags were distributed that they were used to break the sentence up into words. I accepted this as an *hypothesis*, and noted that E was represented by

'But now came the real difficulty of the inquiry. The order of the English letters after E is by no means well marked, and any *preponderance* which may be shown in an average of a printed sheet may be reversed in a single short sentence. Speaking roughly, T, A, O, I, N, S, H, R, D, and L are the numerical order in which the letters occur; but T, A, O, and I are very nearly abreast of each other, and it would be an endless task to try each combination until a meaning was arrived at. I, therefore, waited for fresh material. In my second interview with Mr Hilton Cubitt he was able to give me two other short sentences and one message, which appeared – since there was no flag – to be a single word. Here are the symbols.

Now, in the single word I have already got the two E's coming second and fourth in a word of five letters. It might be "sever" or "lever", or "never". There can be no question that the latter as a reply to an appeal is far the most

hypothesis: a theory formed to account for a number of known facts
preponderance: greater number

probable, and the circumstances pointed to its being a reply written by the lady. Accepting it as correct, we are now able to say that the symbols

stand respectively for N, V, and R.

'Even now I was in considerable difficulty, but a happy thought put me in possession of several other letters. It occurred to me that if these appeals came, as I expected, from someone who had been intimate with the lady in her early life, a combination which contained two E's with three letters between might very well stand for the name "ELSIE". On examination I found that such a combination formed the termination of the message which was three times repeated. It was certainly some appeal to "Elsie". In this way I had got my L, S, and I. But what appeal could it be? There were only four letters in the word which preceded "Elsie", and it ended in E. Surely the word must be "COME". I tried all other four letters ending in E, but could find none to fit the case. So now I was in possession of C, O, and M, and I was in a position to attack the first message once more, dividing it into words and putting dots for each symbol which was still unknown. So treated it worked out in this fashion:

. M .ERE .. E SL . NE .

'Now the first letter can only be A, which is a most useful discovery, since it occurs no fewer than three times in this short sentence, and the H is also apparent in the second word. Now it becomes:

AM HERE A . E SLANE .

Or, filling in the obvious vacancies in the name:

AM HERE ABE SLANEY

I had so many letters now that I could proceed with considerable confidence to the second message, which worked out in this fashion:

A. ELRI . ES

---

formed the termination: came at the end
fashion: manner

COMMENTARY
Holmes continues to explain how he solved the code. He goes on to show how he has discovered that a man named Abe Slaney, who has been staying at Elrige's farm, has been sending the notes.

Here I could only make sense by putting T and G for the missing letters, and supposing that the name was that of some house or inn at which the writer was staying.'

Inspector Martin and I had listened with the utmost interest to the full and clear account of how my friend had produced results which had led to so complete a command over our difficulties.

'What did you do then, sir?' asked the inspector.

'I had every reason to suppose that this Abe Slaney was an American, since Abe is an American contraction, and since a letter from America had been the starting-point of all the trouble. I had also every cause to think that there was some criminal secret in the matter. The lady's allusions to her past and her refusal to take her husband into her confidence both pointed in that direction. I therefore cabled to my friend, Wilson Hargreave, of the New York Police Bureau, who has more than once made use of my knowledge of London crime. I asked him whether the name of Abe Slaney was known to him. Here is his reply: "The most dangerous crook in Chicago." On the very evening upon which I had his answer Hilton Cubitt sent me the last message from Slaney. Working with known letters it took this form:

ELSIE . RE . ARE TO MEET THY GO .

The addition of a P and a D completed a message which showed me that the rascal was proceeding from persuasion to threats, and my knowledge of the crooks of Chicago prepared me to find that he might very rapidly put his words into action. I at once came to Norfolk with my friend and colleague, Dr Watson, but, unhappily, only in time to find that the worst had already occurred.'

'It is a privilege to be associated with you in the handling of a case,' said the inspector, warmly. 'You will excuse me, however, if I speak frankly to you. You are only answerable to yourself, by I have to answer to my superiors. If this Abe Slaney, living at Elrige's, is indeed the murderer, and if he has made his escape while I am seated here, I should certainly get into serious trouble.'

'You need not be uneasy. He will not try to escape.'

'How do you know?'

'To fly would be a confession of guilt.'

COMMENTARY

Holmes has deduced that Abe Slaney was a figure from the past of whom Elsie was ashamed. He reveals that the last note, of which Hilton Cubitt had sent him a copy, contained a threat to Elsie's life, and that is why he hurried down to Norfolk. Inspector Martin is all for going to arrest Abe Slaney, but Holmes says that he has sent him a message which will bring him to the house.

contraction: a shortened form of a name

'Then let us go to arrest him.'

'I expect him here every instant.'

'But why should he come?'

'Because I have written and asked him.'

'But this is incredible, Mr Holmes! Why should he come because you have asked him? Would not such a request rather rouse his suspicions and cause him to fly?'

'I think I have known how to frame the letter,' said Sherlock Holmes. 'In fact, if I am not very much mistaken, here is the gentleman himself coming up the drive.'

A man was striding up the path which led to the door. He was a tall, handsome, swarthy fellow, clad in a suit of grey flannel, with a Panama hat, a bristling black beard and a great, aggressive, hooked nose, and flourishing a cane as he walked. He swaggered up the path as if the place belonged to him, and we heard his loud, confident peal at the bell.

'I think, gentlemen,' said Holmes quietly, 'that we had best take up our position behind the door. Every precaution is necessary when dealing with such a fellow. You will need your handcuffs, Inspector. You can leave the talking to me.'

We waited in silence for a minute – one of those minutes which one can never forget. Then the door opened, and the man stepped in. In an instant Holmes clapped a pistol to his head, and Martin slipped the handcuffs over his wrists. It was all done so swiftly and deftly that the fellow was helpless before he knew that he was attacked. He glared from one to the other of us with a pair of blazing black eyes. Then he burst into a bitter laugh.

'Well, gentlemen, you have the drop on me this time. I seem to have knocked up against something hard. But I came here in answer to a letter from Mrs Hilton Cubitt. Don't tell me that she is in this? Don't tell me that she has helped to set a trap for me?'

'Mrs Hilton Cubitt was seriously injured and is at death's door.'

The man gave a hoarse cry of grief which rang through the house.

'You're crazy!' he cried, fiercely. 'It was he that was hurt, not she. Who

swarthy: dark-complexioned
clad: dressed
swaggered: strutted with pride
clapped: pointed
have the drop on me: have me at a
   disadvantage

COMMENTARY
Just then Slaney arrives. As he walks into the room, Inspector Martin arrests him and puts him in handcuffs. Slaney is very upset to find that Elsie is dangerously wounded.

would have hurt little Elsie? I may have threatened her, God forgive me, but I would not have touched a hair of her pretty head. Take it back – you! Say that she is not hurt!'

'She was found badly wounded by the side of her dead husband.'

He sank with a deep groan on to the settee and buried his face in his manacled hands. For five minutes he was silent. Then he raised his face once more, and spoke with the cold composure of despair.

'I have nothing to hide from you, gentlemen,' said he. 'If I shot the man he had his shot at me, and there's no murder in that. But if you think I could have hurt that woman, then you don't know either me or her. I tell you there was never a man in this world loved a woman more than I loved her. I had a right to her. She was pledged to me years ago. Who was this Englishman that he should come between us? I tell you that I had the first right to her, and that I was only claiming my own.'

'She broke away from your influence when she found the man that you are,' said Holmes sternly. 'She fled from America to avoid you, and she married an honourable gentleman in England. You dogged her and followed her, and made her life a misery to her in order to induce her to abandon the husband whom she loved and respected in order to fly with you, whom she feared and hated. You have ended by bringing about the death of a noble man and driving his wife to suicide. That is your record in this business, Mr Abe Slaney, and you will answer for it to the law.'

'If Elsie dies I care nothing what becomes of me,' said the American. He opened one of his hands and looked at a note crumpled up in his palm. 'See here, mister,' he cried, with a gleam of suspicion in his eyes, 'you're not trying to scare me over this, are you? If the lady is hurt as bad as you say, who was it that wrote this note?' He tossed it forward on to the table.

'I wrote it to bring you here.'

'You wrote it? There was no one on earth outside the Joint who knew the secret of the dancing men. How came you to write it?'

'What one man can invent another can discover,' said Holmes. 'There is a

COMMENTARY

Slaney offers to reveal what happened on the previous night. He says that Elsie was promised to him, and that Hilton Cubitt had no right to come between them.

He is amazed that it was Holmes who wrote the letter that brought him to the house, since he thought that the code Holmes used was a secret known only to members of his gang.

manacled: handcuffed
composure: calm, controlled behaviour
pledged: promised in marriage
dogged: pestered
induce: persuade
the Joint: the name of the gang to which
   Slaney belonged

cab coming to convey you to Norwich, Mr Slaney. But, meanwhile, you have time to make some small reparation for the injury you have wrought. Are you aware that Mrs Hilton Cubitt has herself lain under grave suspicion of the murder of her husband, and that it was only my presence here and the knowledge which I happened to possess which has saved her from the accusation? The least that you owe her is to make it clear to the whole world that she was in no way, directly or indirectly, responsible for his tragic end.'

'I ask nothing better,' said the American. 'I guess the very best case I can make for myself is the absolute naked truth.'

'It is my duty to warn you that it will be used against you,' cried the inspector, with the magnificent fair-play of the British criminal law.

Slaney shrugged his shoulders.

'I'll chance that,' said he. 'First of all, I want you gentlemen to understand that I have known this lady since she was a child. There were seven of us in a gang in Chicago, and Elsie's father was the boss of the Joint. He was a clever man, was old Patrick. It was he who invented that writing, which would pass as a child's scrawl unless you just happened to have the key to it. Well, Elsie learned some of our ways; but she couldn't stand the business, and she had a bit of honest money of her own, so she gave us all the slip and got away to London. She had been engaged to me, and she would have married me, I believe, if I had taken over another profession; but she would have nothing to do with anything on the cross. It was only after her marriage to this Englishman that I was able to find out where she was. I wrote to her, but got no answer. After that I came over, and, as letters were no use, I put my messages where she could read them.

'Well, I have been here a month now. I lived in that farm, where I had a room down below, and could get in and out every night, and no one the wiser. I tried all I could to coax Elsie away. I knew that she read the messages, for once she wrote an answer under one of them. Then my temper got the better of me, and I began to threaten her. She sent me a letter then, imploring me to go away, and saying that it would break her heart if any scandal should come

reparation: amends
on the cross: criminal
coax: pursuade
imploring: begging

COMMENTARY
Slaney explains that Elsie's father ran a criminal gang in Chicago, of which he, Slaney, had been a member. Slaney had wanted to marry Elsie, but she hated everything criminal, and left America to get away from the whole business. In England she married Hilton Cubitt, but Slaney tracked her down and tried to get her back.

upon her husband. She said that she would come down when her husband was asleep at three in the morning, and speak with me through the end window, if I would go away afterwards and leave her in peace. She came down and brought money with her, trying to bribe me to go. This made me mad, and I caught her arm and tried to pull her through the window. At that moment in rushed the husband with his revolver in his hand. Elsie had sunk down upon the floor, and we were face to face. I was heeled also, and I held up my gun to scare him off and let me get away. He fired and missed me. I pulled off almost at the same instant, and down he dropped. I made away across the garden, and as I went I heard the window shut behind me. That's God's truth, gentlemen, every word of it, and I heard no more about it until that lad came riding up with a note which made me walk in here, like a jay, and give myself into your hands.'

A cab had driven up whilst the American had been talking. Two uniformed policemen sat inside. Inspector Martin rose and touched his prisoner on the shoulder.

'It is time for us to go.'

'Can I see her first?'

'No, she is not conscious. Mr Sherlock Holmes, I hope that if ever again I have an important case I shall have the good fortune to have you by my side. '

We stood at the window and watched the cab drive away. As I turned back my eye caught the pellet of paper which the prisoner had tossed upon the table. It was the note with which Holmes had decoyed him.

'See if you can read it, Watson,' said he, with a smile.

It contained no word, but this little line of dancing men:

COMMENTARY

Slaney went to the house to try to get Elsie back, but Cubitt saw him and fired at him. Slaney returned fire in self defence, killing Cubitt, and then ran off.

Inspector Martin takes Slaney away to prison, and Watson tries to puzzle out the note Holmes sent to Slaney.

heeled: carrying a gun

decoyed: trapped

'If you use the code which I have explained,' said Holmes, 'you will find that it simply means "Come here at once." I was convinced that it was an invitation which he would not refuse, since he could never imagine that it could come from anyone but the lady. And so, my dear Watson, we have ended by turning the dancing men to good when they have so often been the agents of evil, and I think that I have fulfilled my promise of giving you something unusual for your note-book. Three-forty is our train, and I fancy we should be back in Baker Street for dinner.'

Only one word of epilogue. The American, Abe Slaney, was condemned to death at the winter assizes at Norwich; but his penalty was changed to penal servitude in consideration of mitigating circumstances, and the certainty that Hilton Cubitt had fired the first shot. Of Mrs Hilton Cubitt I only know that I have heard she recovered entirely, and that she still remains a widow, devoting her whole life to the care of the poor and to the administration of her husband's estate.

PAUSE FOR PLAYBACK:
Now look at the playback questions on page 99.

---

fancy: imagine
epilogue: conclusion
assizes: court
penalty: punishment
penal servitude: imprisonment with hard labour
administration: management

COMMENTARY
Holmes and Watson return to London, Slaney is sent to prison, and Elsie Cubitt recovers to spend the rest of her life helping the poor and looking after her dead husband's house and land.

Study guide

PLAYBACK QUESTIONS

PAGES 71 TO 89:

➤ Elsie Cubitt says on page 74, 'I have had some very disagreeable associations in my life.' How do you think the dancing men may be linked with her past?

➤ What impressions of Hilton Cubitt have you formed so far? Do he and Elsie sound as if they are well-matched married couple?

➤ 'They are shot, both Mr Hilton Cubitt and his wife. She shot him and then herself…' (page 82). Do you think the station-master is likely to be right?

➤ What do you imagine Holmes has put in the note he sends to Abe Slaney? How do you predict Slaney will react when he receives it?

Now return to reading the story on page 90

PAGES 90 TO 98:

➤ What do you think Abe Slaney was telling Elsie in his last message to her (page 93)? What might his purpose have been in sending it?

➤ 'Don't tell me that she has helped to set a trap for me.' (page 94) *Has* Elsie 'set a trap' for Slaney? If so, why?

➤ Abe Slaney seems devastated when he hears that Elsie is near to death and may not recover. Do you think his reaction is a genuine one?

➤ By the end of the story, do you feel that all the main characters have got their just deserts?

➤ In your opinion, has Holmes conducted the case well?

Reviewing the whole story: suggested activities

1   A picture of Elsie's life

Throughout this activity, your role is that of Elsie Cubitt's biographer. Some of the information you supply will come directly from the story. Other details will emerge from 'reading between the lines' and from using your imagination.

a   **As a class**, look back over the story as a whole and draw a time-line showing all the major events in Elsie's life, from her childhood in Chicago to her life as a widow in Norfolk.

b   **With a partner**, re-read closely the following two passages:

● the account which Hilton Cubitt gives of his meeting with, and marriage to, Elsie Patrick (pages 74 to 75);

● the account which Abe Slaney gives of Elsie's early life (page 96).

Working together, make notes on (i) everything you can learn about Elsie's early life and her attitude towards it, (ii) why she came to England and (iii) her feelings for her husband.

c   **By yourself**, imagine that Elsie has kept a private diary all her life, from the time she was a girl until she became a widow. Choose what seem to you to be the five key moments in her life, and write her diary entries for those days.

Try to bring out not only 'what happened', but also how she feels about the events she describes.

2 | Code breaking

The key to solving the case of *The Dancing Men* is the breaking of a code. This activity asks you to show your understanding of the code in the story, then to experiment with writing coded messages of your own.

a   **By yourself**, re-read pages 90 to 93 where Holmes describes how he broke the code of 'the dancing men'.

b   Then draw two vertical columns. In the first, write down all the letters of the alphabet. Opposite to them, write the dancing-men symbols as they are shown in the story.

   Bear in mind that there are eight letters – F, J, K, Q, U, W, X and Z – unaccounted for.

c   **As a class**, agree on dancing-men symbols for the 'missing' eight letters, so that everyone has a complete coded alphabet.

d   **With a partne**r, write together a secret message using the dancing-men code. Do not make it too long, and remember to put in the little flags where the words end.

e   Exchange your message with another pair. Each pair should decipher the other's message and check the solution.

   There are all sorts of codes based on the alphabet. Some use symbols, such as the dancing men. Some use the dots and dashes of the Morse code. Others use the letters of the alphabet in a different way. You can, for instance, make a code simply by shifting each letter forward by one character, so that B stands for A, C stands for B, and so on through the alphabet until you get back to A. (What will A stand for in this code?)

f   **By yourself**, invent an alphabet code. Use either letters or symbols. After working out the whole alphabet in your code, write a message in it at least two sentences long.

g   Exchange messages **with a partner**. Try to decode what the other person has written.

At each stage of the decoding process, make notes to explain your partner's code by making a flow chart like the one set out below.

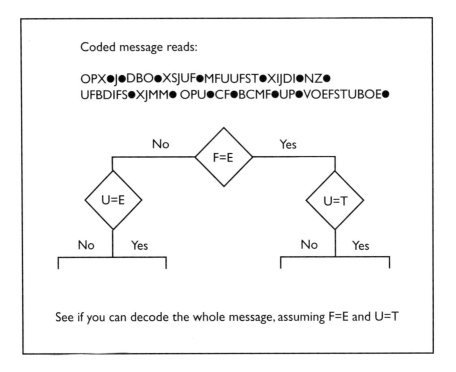

Coded message reads:

OPX●J●DBO●XSJUF●MFUUFST●XIJDI●NZ●
UFBDIFS●XJMM● OPU●CF●BCMF●UP●VOEFSTUBOE●

No   ╱F=E╲   Yes

╱U=E╲   ╱U=T╲

No | Yes   No | Yes

See if you can decode the whole message, assuming F=E and U=T

When you have decoded your partner's message, note down how many 'false turns' you took before you solved it.

h   **As a class**, compare the various codes people have invented. You can put them together into a 'code book', with an introduction about making and breaking codes – or you can mount them as a class display.

3 A scripted interview

Although Elsie is central to the story of *The Dancing Men*, we never actually meet her.

a   **By yourself**, script an interview between Elsie and Sherlock Holmes, in which he explains to her how he came to be involved in the case and how he solved it. You will have to invent your own details of what she looks like and how she behaves.

When writing, stay as close as possible to the language and style of Dr Watson's account. Before you begin, ask yourself the following: given the kind of background that Elsie has come from, what attitude will Holmes have to her – and how will this affect the way he speaks to her?

b **With a partner**, act out each other's scripts, taking it in turn to play Holmes and Elsie.

OTHER RECOMMENDED SHERLOCK HOLMES STORIES

The Five Orange Pips

The Man with the Twisted Lip

The Blue Carbuncle

The Engineer's Thumb

The Beryl Coronet

The Copper Beeches

The Solitary Cyclist

The Priory School

Black Peter

The Lion's Mane

His Last Bow

You can find these stories in *The Complete Penguin Sherlock Holmes* (Penguin, 1981).

Overview

1 | A Sherlock Holmes case index

On page 16 of *A Scandal in Bohemia*, Sherlock Holmes refers to his 'index', where he keeps information about cases in which he has been involved and the characters he has investigated.

a   **As a class**, go through all three stories in this volume. Make one complete list of the characters who play an important part in them and the places with which they are connected.

b   **With a partner**, organise this list into alphabetical order.

c   **By yourself**, look back to the stories and retrieve all the information you can find about each of the alphabetical entries on the list. Write it down in full sentences using formal Standard English.

d   If you have the opportunity, put your information onto a database and print it out. Give it the title 'Sherlock Holmes's Index of People and Places'.

2 | Building up the evidence

In England, when the police take someone to court for a criminal offence they have to submit all their evidence to the Director of Public Prosecutions (DPP). The DPP decides whether there is enough evidence for the accused to be required to stand trial.

By yourself, choose one of the stories from this volume. Quickly read it through again. Then note down (i) the evidence it gives that a crime has been committed and (ii) *all* the evidence there is against the chief suspect.

Imagine you are a police officer. Use your notes to compile the report which you will send to the DPP. You will need to provide:

●   a summary of all the events that have occurred;

●   transcripts of any interviews you have had with the accused;

●   a list of all the material evidence against the accused (footprints, fingerprints, etc).

You could also include illustrations showing pictures of the main people involved in the case, maps of the most important locations, 'photographs' of exhibits (ropes, guns, bullets, bullet-holes, etc.).

Your report will need to be written in formal Standard English. It should be clearly set out, including headings and sub-headings, as well as an index.

3 | A woman's place

In all three stories in this volume, a central part is played by women: Irene Adler, Helen Stoner and Elsie Cubitt.

If you have read all of the stories, you may have noticed that Conan Doyle seems to have had a very particular view of what women should be like, how they should behave, and what they deserve if they do not behave 'properly'.

a   **As a class**, look through all the three stories and note down everything that you can find out about the women in them. Organise your notes under the following headings:

- appearance;

- social class;

- innocence;

- their response to events (do they take action themselves, or are they acted upon?);

- how they end up.

b   **With a partner**, draw five bar charts for the three women, showing how they rate on a scale of 1 to 20 for the following features:

- beautiful/plain and uninteresting;

- upper class/working class;

- innocent/experienced;

- active/passive;

- ends happily/ends unhappily or dead.

Your first bar chart might look like this:

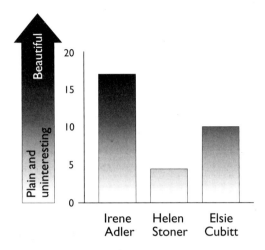

c **By yourself**, look carefully at your bar charts. Use them to summarise in a paragraph or two what they tell you about the qualities Conan Doyle valued in and expected of women.

d Then write two further paragraphs, one summing up the writer's attitude to women in general and the other putting forward your own response to his view of them.

4 'My Dear Watson'

All of the stories in this volume are narrated by Dr Watson. Since he is the story-teller, we get only an indirect view of what he is like – through, for example:

● his reactions to Holmes's powers as a detective and to the way Holmes conducts his investigations;

● his comments on the major characters in the stories and on their behaviour;

● his sense of right and wrong;

● his tone of voice as he tells each story.

a **As a class**, talk about the kind of person Watson is. Refer closely to particular passages in the stories you have read to back up your impressions of his character.

b **By yourself**, imagine that Holmes is writing to a friend who has never met Watson. The friend has asked Holmes for an account of what Watson is *really* like.

Write Holmes's letter describing his close friend, the man who has been his loyal companion and helper in solving so many of the great detective's cases.

Since Holmes is writing quite informally to a friend, you can decide just how open and honest he will be in giving his opinions about Watson and in summing up his character. The letter will be more realistic if it includes examples of Watson's behaviour drawn from the stories in this volume.

5 Rough justice?

At the end of *The Speckled Band,* we are told that Holmes did not regret the fact that the criminal died before he could be brought to justice (see page 65). There is, throughout the stories in this volume, a feeling that Holmes operates outside the conventional legal system.

How important do you think it is that the legal system should be observed in every case, even if it means some criminals escaping justice?

a **By yourself**, make notes on what you think about this question. (If your teacher feels it will be helpful, first discuss this issue in a group). Where you can, use evidence from the stories in this volume to back up your views, but feel free to move beyond the stories to other examples about which you may know.

b Then, **as a class**, hold a formal debate on the following subject:

'A healthy society is one in which wrongdoers will always fear punishment, either within or beyond what the law allows.'

c **By yourself**, write a response to the following extract, which is taken from a letter to a newspaper. Give your own views on any or all of the issues it raises.

'In today's society, crime of all kinds is on the increase. An over-stretched police force cannot be expected to cope with the rising tide of crime, ranging from house burglaries to major drug-rackets. We need additional forms of law-enforcement to prevent our country from becoming completely lawless.'